DEFENSE, SECURITY AND STRATEGIES

UNMANNED AERIAL SYSTEMS

PILOT AND PERSONNEL ISSUES

DEFENSE, SECURITY AND STRATEGIES

Additional books in this series can be found on Nova's website
under the Series tab.

Additional e-books in this series can be found on Nova's website
under the e-book tab.

DEFENSE, SECURITY AND STRATEGIES

UNMANNED AERIAL SYSTEMS

PILOT AND PERSONNEL ISSUES

LISSA BARLOW
EDITOR

nova publishers

New York

NOTICE TO THE READER

The Publisher has taken reasonable care in the preparation of this book, but makes no expressed or implied warranty of any kind and assumes no responsibility for any errors or omissions. No liability is assumed for incidental or consequential damages in connection with or arising out of information contained in this book. The Publisher shall not be liable for any special, consequential, or exemplary damages resulting, in whole or in part, from the readers' use of, or reliance upon, this material. Any parts of this book based on government reports are so indicated and copyright is claimed for those parts to the extent applicable to compilations of such works.

Independent verification should be sought for any data, advice or recommendations contained in this book. In addition, no responsibility is assumed by the publisher for any injury and/or damage to persons or property arising from any methods, products, instructions, ideas or otherwise contained in this publication.

This publication is designed to provide accurate and authoritative information with regard to the subject matter covered herein. It is sold with the clear understanding that the Publisher is not engaged in rendering legal or any other professional services. If legal or any other expert assistance is required, the services of a competent person should be sought. FROM A DECLARATION OF PARTICIPANTS JOINTLY ADOPTED BY A COMMITTEE OF THE AMERICAN BAR ASSOCIATION AND A COMMITTEE OF PUBLISHERS.

Additional color graphics may be available in the e-book version of this book.

Library of Congress Cataloging-in-Publication Data

ISBN: 978-1-63321-474-3

Published by Nova Science Publishers, Inc. † New York

CONTENTS

Preface   **vii**

Chapter 1   Air Force: Actions Needed to Strengthen Management
of Unmanned Aerial System Pilots   **1**
United States Government Accountability Office

Chapter 2   Unmanned Aircraft Systems: Comprehensive Planning
and a Results-Oriented Training Strategy Are Needed
to Support Growing Inventories   **49**
United States Government Accountability Office

Chapter 3   Facets of Occupational Burnout Among U.S. Air Force
Active Duty and National Guard/Reserve MQ-1
Predator and MQ-9 Reaper Operators   **97**
Joseph A. Ouma, Wayne L. Chappelle
and Amber Salinas

Index   **121**

PREFACE

The Air Force has managed its remotely piloted aircraft (RPA) pilots using some strategic human-capital approaches, such as planning for the different levels of experience that it needs in these pilots. However, it continues to face challenges. This book evaluates the extent to which the Air Force has used a strategic human-capital approach to manage RPA pilots; addresses concerns, if any, about the working conditions of RPA pilots that may affect their quality of life; and analyzes the promotion rates of RPA pilots. It also discusses the extent to which plans were in place to account for the personnel, facilities, and communications infrastructure needed to support Air Force and Army UAS inventories. Challenges that affect the ability of the Air Force and the Army to train personnel for UAS operations are also addressed.

Chapter 1 – Since 2008, the Air Force has more than tripled the number of its active- duty pilots flying RPAs, which is the term the Air Force uses to refer to unmanned aerial systems such as the MQ-1 Predator. Due to increases in demand, RPA pilots have had a significant increase in workload since 2007. GAO was asked to evaluate the Air Force's approach to managing its RPA pilots as well as their quality of life and promotion rates. For this review, GAO evaluated the extent to which the Air Force (1) has used a strategic human-capital approach to manage RPA pilots; (2) has addressed concerns, if any, about the working conditions of RPA pilots that may affect their quality of life; and (3) analyzes the promotion rates of RPA pilots.

GAO analyzed personnel planning documents, Air Force studies, and officer promotion data. GAO also interviewed unit commanders at selected Air Force bases and Headquarters Air Force officials and conducted focus groups with RPA pilots. While the results of these focus groups are not generalizable, they provide valuable insights.

Chapter 2 – The Department of Defense (DOD) requested about $6.1 billion in fiscal year 2010 for new unmanned aircraft systems (UAS) and for expanded capabilities in existing ones. To support ongoing operations, the Air Force and Army have acquired a greater number of larger systems. GAO was asked to determine the extent to which (1) plans were in place to account for the personnel, facilities, and communications infrastructure needed to support Air Force and Army UAS inventories; (2) DOD addressed challenges that affect the ability of the Air Force and the Army to train personnel for UAS operations; and (3) DOD updated its publications that articulate doctrine and tactics, techniques, and procedures to reflect the knowledge gained from using UAS in ongoing operations. Focusing on UAS programs supporting ongoing operations, GAO reviewed the services' program and funding plans in light of DOD's requirements definition and acquisition policy; interviewed UAS personnel in the United States and in Iraq about training experiences; and reviewed joint, multiservice, and service-specific publications.

Chapter 3 – The increasing operational demand for MQ-1 Predator and MQ-9 Reaper remotely piloted aircraft (RPA) in support of intelligence, surveillance, and reconnaissance missions as well as precision-strike operations in theaters of conflict has led to a substantial rise in operational hours, shift work, and exposure to combat-related events (e.g., destruction of enemy assets and combatants) for operators. As a result of the continual need to sustain a high operational tempo, there are concerns among line commanders and aeromedical leadership regarding the prevalence of occupational burnout. There is also concern that there are differences across units for risk of occupational burnout and that active duty crew members are at higher risk when compared with National Guard/Reserve operators. This study surveyed 426 officer and enlisted operators (pilots and sensor operators). Although a wide range of stressors may contribute to elevated levels of burnout, the majority of occupational stress was reported to stem from operational stress and not exposure to combat (e.g., live video feed regarding the destruction or death of enemy combatants and ground forces). In general, the results revealed that active duty operators are more than twice as likely to suffer from the facets of occupational burnout involving emotional exhaustion and cynicism. Active duty as well as National Guard/Reserve operators attributed shift work, shift changes, hours worked, and simultaneously serving as a warfighter in theater while returning home and managing domestic roles and responsibilities at home to their burnout levels. Aeromedical recommendations include reducing operational hours, reducing frequency of shift changes, reducing the length of assignments, providing clear guidance and opportunities for competitive career-progression, improving human-machine interfacing within the ground control station, marital and family enrichment opportunities, as well as periodic psychological health assessments to mitigate the risk of burnout among RPA operators.

In: Unmanned Aerial Systems
Editor: Lissa Barlow

ISBN: 978-1-63321-474-3
© 2014 Nova Science Publishers, Inc.

Chapter 1

AIR FORCE: ACTIONS NEEDED TO STRENGTHEN MANAGEMENT OF UNMANNED AERIAL SYSTEM PILOTS[*]

United States Government Accountability Office

WHY GAO DID THIS STUDY

Since 2008, the Air Force has more than tripled the number of its active-duty pilots flying RPAs, which is the term the Air Force uses to refer to unmanned aerial systems such as the MQ-1 Predator. Due to increases in demand, RPA pilots have had a significant increase in workload since 2007. GAO was asked to evaluate the Air Force's approach to managing its RPA pilots as well as their quality of life and promotion rates. For this review, GAO evaluated the extent to which the Air Force (1) has used a strategic human-capital approach to manage RPA pilots; (2) has addressed concerns, if any, about the working conditions of RPA pilots that may affect their quality of life; and (3) analyzes the promotion rates of RPA pilots.

GAO analyzed personnel planning documents, Air Force studies, and officer promotion data. GAO also interviewed unit commanders at selected Air Force bases and Headquarters Air Force officials and conducted focus

---

[*] This is an edited, reformatted and augmented version of the United States Government Accountability Office publication, GAO-14-316, dated April 2014.

groups with RPA pilots. While the results of these focus groups are not generalizable, they provide valuable insights.

WHAT GAO RECOMMENDS

GAO recommends that the Air Force update optimum crew ratios; establish a minimum crew ratio; develop a recruiting and retention strategy; evaluate using alternative personnel populations to be pilots; use feedback from RPA pilots; analyze the effects of being deployed-on-station; and analyze the effect that being an RPA pilot has on promotions. The Air Force concurred with four recommendations and partially concurred with the remaining three recommendations.

WHAT GAO FOUND

The Air Force has managed its remotely piloted aircraft (RPA) pilots using some strategic human-capital approaches, such as planning for the different levels of experience that it needs in these pilots. However, it continues to face challenges. High-performing organizations manage human capital to identify the right number of personnel and to target the right sources to fill personnel needs. In 2008, the Air Force determined the optimum number of RPA pilots—the crew ratio—for some units, but it did not account for all tasks these units complete. Air Force officials stated that, as a result, the crew ratio is too low, but the Air Force has not updated it. Air Force guidance states that low crew ratios diminish combat capability and cause flight safety to suffer, but the Air Force has operated below its optimum crew ratio and it has not established a minimum crew ratio. Further, high work demands on RPA pilots limit the time they have available for training and development and negatively affects their work-life balance. In addition, the Air Force faces challenges recruiting officers into the RPA pilot career and may face challenges retaining them in the future. High-performing organizations tailor their recruiting and retention strategies to meet their specific mission needs, but the Air Force has not tailored its approach to recruiting and retaining RPA pilots nor considered the viability of using alternative personnel such as enlisted personnel or civilians. Without developing an approach to recruiting and retaining RPA pilots and evaluating the viability of using alternative personnel populations for the RPA pilot career, the Air Force may continue to face challenges, further exacerbating existing shortfalls of RPA pilots. Moreover, the Air Force has not used direct feedback from RPA pilots via existing mechanisms, or otherwise, to develop its approach to managing challenges related to recruiting, retention, training, and development of RPA pilots.

The Air Force has taken some actions to address potentially difficult working conditions RPA pilots face, but it has not fully analyzed the challenge pilots face to balance their warfighting roles with their personal lives. RPA pilots operate RPAs from bases in the United States and live at home; thus they experience combat alongside their personal lives—known as being deployed-on-station— which RPA pilots stated negatively affects their morale. While the Department of Defense has committed to maintaining high morale for servicemembers, the Air Force has not fully analyzed the effects on morale related to being deployed-on- station, and thus it does not know whether it needs to take actions in response.

The Air Force monitors RPA pilot promotion rates, but has not analyzed factors that may relate to their low promotion rates. Statistical principles call for researchers to account for potential key factors in analysis because when they omit key factors, the relationships between other factors may not be accurately estimated. The Air Force analyzed promotions across a group of officers, including RPA pilots, and found factors that related to promotions in general. However, the Air Force has not analyzed the factors related to RPA pilots' promotions specifically and, as a result, it does not have the information to determine what factors may affect their promotions. Consequently, the Air Force may not be targeting actions it is taking to raise RPA pilot promotion rates at the appropriate factors, and information it has reported to Congress may not be accurate.

ABBREVIATIONS

AFPC	Air Force Personnel Center
CAP	combat air patrol
DOD	Department of Defense
DOPMA	Defense Officer Personnel Management Act
RPA	remotely piloted aircraft

April 10, 2014

The Honorable Harry Reid
Majority Leader
United States Senate

The Honorable Carl Levin
Chairman
Committee on Armed Services
United States Senate

Remotely piloted aircraft (RPA) are one of the most in-demand capabilities the Air Force provides to battlefield commanders.[1] Beyond replacing human beings in aircraft that perform dangerous roles, RPAs are highly valuable because they possess characteristics that many manned aircraft do not. For example, they can fly long-duration missions, thereby providing a sustained presence over the battlefield. In response to the increased demand, the Air Force has significantly increased the number of RPAs it uses for intelligence, surveillance, and reconnaissance and precision strike capabilities, according to Air Force documentation. Consequently, the Air Force has increased the number of its pilots flying RPAs from approximately 400 in 2008 to about 1,350 in 2013. Due to the increased demand for their capabilities, these pilots have served at a high pace of operations since 2007.[2] Most of these pilots are located on Air Force bases within the United States and fly the RPAs overseas in operational environments. The Air Force uses the term RPA to refer to large unmanned aircraft systems, such as the MQ-1 Predator. The Department of Defense (DOD) defines an unmanned aerial system as a system whose components include the necessary equipment, networks, and personnel to control an unmanned aircraft—that is, an aircraft that does not carry a human operator and is capable of flight under remote control or autonomous programming.

Our prior work has found that DOD has faced challenges in the development and acquisition of unmanned aircraft systems and in the integration of these systems into combat operations.[3] Regarding personnel, we have found that the Air Force and the Army identified limitations in their approaches to provide personnel to meet unmanned aircraft systems force levels, and they had not fully developed plans to supply needed personnel.[4] More recently, the National Defense Authorization Act for Fiscal Year 2013[5] required the Air Force to report on the education, training, and promotion rates of RPA pilots.

You requested that we evaluate the Air Force's approach to managing its RPA pilot workforce as well as the pilots' quality of life and their promotion rates. For this review we evaluated the extent to which the Air Force (1) has used a strategic human-capital approach to manage RPA pilots; (2) has addressed concerns, if any, about the working conditions of RPA pilots that may affect their quality of life; and (3) has analyzed the promotion rates of RPA pilots.

To evaluate the extent to which the Air Force uses a strategic human-capital approach to manage RPA pilots, we applied criteria from our model of strategic human-capital management that we previously reported. The model includes leading practices used by high-performing organizations and is intended to help federal organizations use their human capital effectively and integrate human-capital considerations into daily decision making and planning for the program results they wish to accomplish.[6] We adapted these criteria by analyzing the practices in the model to determine which were relevant to RPA pilots and a military career in general. We reviewed our adaptation with Air Force officials who agreed that our criteria were relevant to the Air Force's management of RPA pilots. To identify the extent to which the Air Force used these practices, we interviewed officials from offices including the Deputy Chief of Staff of the Air Force for Manpower, Personnel, and Services and the Deputy Chief of Staff of the Air Force for Operations, Plans, and Requirements, as well as RPA pilots and their commanders. In addition, we analyzed DOD and Air Force guidance and data on personnel levels, incentive pays, and attrition rates for RPA pilots. Furthermore, we discussed instances of Air Force personnel-management actions that we found to be inconsistent with the leading practices we reported on previously with the appropriate Air Force officials.

To evaluate the extent to which the Air Force has addressed concerns, if any, about the working conditions of RPA pilots that may affect their quality of life, we identified and analyzed criteria included in DOD's 2009 and 2004 *Quadrennial Quality of Life Reviews*. These reviews include statements that express DOD's commitment to provide servicemembers with the best quality of life possible. DOD has broadly defined quality of life to include such factors as morale, health and wellness, and work-life balance. To understand the working conditions of RPA pilots that may affect their quality of life, we analyzed Air Force studies that evaluated the stress and mental-health conditions of RPA personnel, which included pilots. We also interviewed the researchers who conducted these studies to clarify our understanding of their methods, findings, and recommendations to alleviate the stress of RPA personnel. We analyzed the recommendations included in the Air Force studies as well as documentation provided by officials from various Air Force offices describing actions the Air Force has taken in response to these recommendations. In addition, we interviewed officials from the Air Force Medical Support Agency, Headquarters Air Force officials, as well as RPA pilots, their commanders, and mental-health professionals during site visits to Beale, Cannon, and Creech Air Force Bases. In these interviews we obtained perspectives on the working conditions of RPA pilots that may affect their quality of life and actions taken in response.

To evaluate the extent to which the Air Force analyzes the promotion rates of RPA pilots, we applied criteria from our model of strategic human-capital management[7] regarding using complete data in human-capital decisions. We analyzed data from the Air Force Personnel Center (AFPC) for active-duty officers promoted to the ranks of major, lieutenant colonel, and colonel. We analyzed data from 2006 to the most-recently available data, which for promotion to major and colonel was 2012 and for promotion to lieutenant colonel was 2013.[8] In addition, we interviewed officials from AFPC, reviewed documentation they provided, and found the data to be reliable for our purposes. Furthermore, we analyzed documentation that officials from Headquarters Air Force and AFPC provided, including Air Force policy that governs the officer promotion process, AFPC's analysis of officer promotion rates, and the Air Force's August 2013 report to Congress on the promotion rates of RPA pilots.[9] Moreover, we evaluated documentation of steps the Air Force has taken to raise the promotion rates of RPA pilots including instructions the Secretary of the Air Force provided to promotion board members and briefings that Headquarters Air Force and AFPC prepared for the Secretary of the Air Force.

For all our objectives, we also conducted 10 focus groups during site visits to Beale, Cannon, and Creech Air Force Bases. Each group generally consisted of six to nine active-duty RPA pilots at ranks ranging from second lieutenant to lieutenant colonel. The information that we obtained during these focus groups accurately captures the opinions provided by the RPA pilots who attended the focus groups at the three Air Force Bases we visited. However, these opinions cannot be generalized to all RPA pilots at these bases or to all RPA pilots in the Air Force. We discuss our scope and methodology in more detail in appendix I and our approach to conducting our focus groups in appendix II.

We conducted this performance audit from February 2013 to April 2014 in accordance with generally accepted government auditing standards. Those standards require that we plan and perform the audit to obtain sufficient, appropriate evidence to provide a reasonable basis for our findings and conclusions based on our audit objectives. We believe that the evidence obtained provides a reasonable basis for our findings and conclusions based on our audit objectives.

BACKGROUND

Growth in Use of RPAs and Expanded Missions

The Air Force has rapidly expanded its use of RPAs in the last decade to support combat operations in Iraq and Afghanistan. The Air Force flies three types of RPAs—the MQ-1 (Predator), the MQ-9 (Reaper) and the larger RQ-4 (Global Hawk). Beyond the traditional intelligence, surveillance, and reconnaissance capability to analyze evolving battlefield conditions, the MQ-1 and the MQ-9 have been outfitted with missiles to strike targets, with equipment to designate targets for manned aircraft by laser, and with sensors to locate the positions of improvised explosive devices and moving insurgents, among other missions.

The Military Services' Various Approaches to Assigning RPA Personnel

All the military services operate RPAs, and each uses different approaches to assign personnel to pilot them and operate their sensors. For example, the Air Force (the focus of this review) assigns officers to fly RPAs and enlisted personnel to operate the RPAs' sensors, which provide intelligence, surveillance, and reconnaissance capabilities. In addition, the Air Force relied solely on manned-aircraft pilots to fly RPAs until 2010, when it established an RPA pilot career field for officers who specialize in flying RPAs and are not qualified to fly manned aircraft. Similarly, the Navy assigns officers to pilot RPAs, and enlisted personnel to operate RPA sensors. However, the Navy has not established a separate career field for pilots who specialize in flying RPAs and instead assigns pilots of manned aircraft to operate them. By contrast, the Army and Marine Corps have opted to assign enlisted personnel to fly RPAs and operate their sensors. Further, in both the Army and Marine Corps, there is no distinction between the pilot and sensor operator.

RPA Pilots' Current and Future Basing

Air Force RPA pilots carry out their missions and pilot RPAs from eight active-duty bases in the continental United States including Creech, Cannon, and Beale Air Force Bases and from Air National Guard bases in six states including North Dakota, New York, and Ohio. In addition, RPA pilots are trained at some of the bases where RPAs are operated, such as at Beale Air Force Base, as well as at other bases where RPAs are not operated, such as at Holloman Air Force Base. The Air Force plans to add an Air Force Reserve unit at Hurlburt Field as well as Air National Guard RPA bases in Arkansas, Iowa, Michigan, New York, and Pennsylvania (see figure 1).

Source: GAO analysis of Air Force documents: Map Resources (map).

Figure 1. Current and Planned Operational and Training Locations for Air Force Pilots of Remotely Piloted Aircraft (RPA).

Training and Training Costs

The initial training that the Air Force provides to its RPA pilots is designed specifically for flying RPAs and consists of two major components that take about 10 months to complete. The first major component is Undergraduate RPA Training and it consists of a basic flying skills course in which RPA pilots learn to fly a small manned aircraft in Pueblo, Colorado; instrument training in a manned-aircraft flight simulator at Randolph Air Force Base in Texas, and an RPA fundamentals course that is also at Randolph. In the second major component of their initial training, RPA pilots get their first opportunity to fly an RPA at a Formal Training Unit, which for most active-duty pilots takes place at Holloman Air Force Base in New Mexico. During this training, RPA pilots learn basic RPA operations in all mission areas including intelligence, surveillance, and reconnaissance as well as close air support. Following their time in Formal Training Units, RPA pilots finish their training by attending a 2- week joint weapons course in which they learn how to operate with the Army, Navy, and Marine Corps in a joint operational environment.

The Air Force spends considerably less to train RPA pilots than it does to train manned-aircraft pilots. Specifically, Air Education and Training Command officials estimate that the Air Force spends about $65,000 to train each RPA pilot to complete Undergraduate RPA Training. Conversely, these officials estimate that the Air Force spends an average of $557,000[10] for each manned-aircraft pilot to complete the corresponding portion of manned-aircraft pilot training, which is called Undergraduate Pilot Training.

Remote-Split Operations

The Air Force currently flies the bulk of its RPAs using a concept known as remote-split operations. With remote-split operations, a small number of RPA pilots deploy to operational theaters located overseas to launch and recover RPAs from various locations around the world while other RPA pilots remotely control the RPA for its mission from Air Force bases in the United States (see figure 2). According to Air Force officials, remote- split operations help the Air Force reduce the personnel and equipment it deploys overseas because the units that launch and recover RPAs are staffed with a relatively small number of pilots, sensor operators, support personnel, and equipment. In addition, remote-split operations provide the Air Force flexibility to change the geographic region of the world where an RPA pilot conducts a mission without moving the pilot, support personnel, or equipment needed to control the RPA. If the Air Force is not able to use one of its launch and recovery sites for various reasons such as poor weather, the Air Force can continue its RPA operations by launching RPAs from a different launch and recovery site.

Promotion Process

The Defense Officer Personnel Management Act (DOPMA)[11] created a system for managing the promotions for the officer corps of each of the military services. DOPMA specifies that the secretaries of the military departments must establish the maximum number of officers in each competitive category that may be recommended for promotion by competitive promotion boards. Career categories, also known as competitive categories, cluster officers with similar education, training, or experience, and these officers compete among themselves for promotion opportunities. Under this system, as currently implemented in the Air Force, there are several competitive categories including one that contains the bulk of Air Force officers called the Line of the Air Force, which includes RPA pilots, as well as pilots of manned aircraft and other operations-oriented careers.[12]

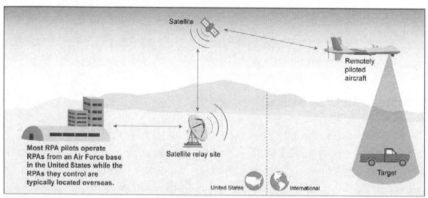

Source: GAO analysis of DOD information.

Figure 2. Remote-Split Operations of Air Force Remotely Piloted Aircraft (RPA).

To consider officers for promotion from among those who are eligible, the Air Force assigns groups of senior officers to serve as members of a promotion selection board for each competitive category of officer in the Air Force.

Promotion boards consist of at least five active-duty officers who are senior in grade to the eligible officers, but no officer on the board is below the rank of major.

In addition, Air Force guidance states that the Air Force attempts to provide a balanced perspective on promotion boards, and hence it selects officers who mirror, as much as possible, the officers they are considering with respect to race, sex, aeronautical rating, career field, and command.[13] Promotion boards typically convene annually at AFPC headquarters to review a variety of records for each eligible officer, including performance and training reports as well as recommendations from supervisors. Board members assess these records using a best-qualified approach and use a variety of methods to score the records and resolve differences among the scoring of the board members, if necessary. An Air Force officer cannot serve as a member of two successive promotion boards considering officers of the same competitive category and rank.

A key feature of DOPMA is its "up-or-out" promotion system. Under this system, as currently implemented in the Air Force, promotion to the first two ranks in an officer's career is not competitive. Specifically, 100 percent of fully qualified Air Force second lieutenants and first lieutenants are promoted after serving for 2 years in their respective ranks and do not meet with a competitive promotion board.

However, as officers advance through the ranks in cohorts that are determined by the year they were commissioned, they compete for promotion against other members of their cohort at set years or zones of consideration for each rank. For example, Air Force officers are generally considered for promotion to major, or the grade of O-4, after 10 years.

Under the DOPMA system, a select group of officers can also be considered for promotion 1 or 2 years early, or "below the zone." However, because only a limited number of officers below the zone may be promoted, officers have their greatest potential for promotion "in the zone." If officers in a cohort are not promoted while they are in the zone, they can compete for promotion in the following one or in some instances two years later, which is known as competing "above the zone."

However, if these officers are not selected for promotion above the zone, they could be involuntarily separated from the Air Force.

THE AIR FORCE HAS MADE EFFORTS TO MANAGE RPA PILOTS BUT FACES CHALLENGES TO RECRUIT, DEVELOP, AND RETAIN PILOTS AND BUILD THEIR MORALE

The Air Force has taken some steps toward managing RPA pilots using a strategic human-capital approach but faces several challenges including accurately identifying personnel requirements, limited training time for pilots, recruiting and retention difficulties, and incorporating feedback from RPA pilots into its operations.

The Air Force Has Undertaken Some Workforce Planning Efforts but It May Not Have Identified Its Personnel Requirements Accurately

The Air Force's effort to meet combatant command RPA requirements has included some elements of strategic human-capital planning, but increasing demand and past experience indicate the Air Force has not accurately identified RPA personnel requirements. High-performing organizations use strategic human-capital planning to help them evaluate the extent to which their human-capital approaches support the accomplishment of programmatic goals. Strategic human-capital planning involves identifying human-capital needs like the necessary "shape," which involves ensuring that agencies have the right numbers of staff at the right levels of experience, as well as the necessary size of the workforce for accomplishing agency missions while also enabling the workforce to accomplish career-development tasks, which furthers agency goals and objectives.

Air Force Steps to Plan for the Shape and Size of the RPA Pilot Workforce and React to Increased Combat Air Patrol (CAP) Requirements

The Air Force has taken steps to plan for the shape and size of the RPA pilot workforce and react to requirements from the Secretary of Defense, including adding a cadre of experienced officers to mentor officers recruited into a new career the Air Force established for RPA pilots. In order to develop a long-term, sustainable career path for pilots flying RPAs and demonstrate its commitment to RPA pilots, in 2010 the Air Force established an RPA pilot career field with a separate set of training requirements. These officers are qualified only to fly RPAs and are not qualified on Air Force manned aircraft.

In addition, the Air Force recognized that as new officers were recruited into the RPA pilot career field, they would need a group of more-senior officers to serve as mentors and leaders. Therefore, in 2011, the Air Force permanently recategorized around 475 manned-aircraft pilots who were generally serving at the ranks of major and lieutenant colonel to serve as permanent RPA pilots, according to Air Force documentation. Air Force officials stated that these more-senior pilots would help provide a leadership and experience base for the new RPA pilot career field. The officials also stated that additional manned-aircraft pilots have been permanently recategorized as RPA pilots since 2011, and Air Force documentation shows a total of 545 recategorized manned-aircraft pilots.

Furthermore, the Air Force has taken steps to plan for the size of its RPA pilot workforce. According to Headquarters Air Force officials, the number of RPA combat air patrols (CAP),[14] directed by the Secretary of Defense and based on the mission needs of the combatant commands, is a primary factor in determining RPA pilot personnel levels. In 2010, the Secretary of Defense directed the Air Force to fund personnel to reach 65 CAPs by fiscal year 2013 and be prepared to grow beyond that requirement in future years. To determine the number of RPA pilots, the Air Force Manpower Agency conducted a personnel requirements study for MQ-1 Predator squadrons in 2008 and established the number of RPA crews required to fly one CAP for 24 hours, referred to as the crew ratio.

Based on the study, the Air Force concluded that the crew ratio for MQ-1 Predator squadrons would be 10:1, which calls for 10 RPA pilots to sustain a Predator for 24 hours.[15] Air Force officials stated that although the 2008 study did not address the personnel requirements for MQ-9 Reaper squadrons, the Air Force used the study as the basis for establishing a 10:1 crew ratio for MQ-9 units also because MQ-1 and MQ-9 units have similar requirements. In addition to this crew ratio, the Air Force used Air Force Instruction 38-201[16] to calculate the required number of additional pilots it needs for support positions such as commanders, and staff positions at various organizational levels including headquarters.[17] Using the crew ratio and the Air Force instruction, the Air Force determined that the total number of RPA pilots required to sustain the 65 CAPs currently required by the Secretary of Defense is between 1,600 and 1,650 pilots, according to a Headquarters Air Force official.

Furthermore, the Air Force has taken steps to react to increased CAP requirements. Until 2009, the Air Force relied solely on manned-aircraft pilots serving assignments as RPA pilots to fill personnel requirements. In fiscal year 2006, manned-aircraft pilots were sustaining 12 CAPs, and the 2006 *Quadrennial Defense Review* stated that the Predator system alone would grow to 21 CAPs by 2010. However, according to Headquarters Air Force officials, by 2007 the demand from the combatant commands had already exceeded that benchmark. Air Force leadership committed the service to meeting the increased requirements, and the Air Force took actions to provide sufficient personnel. These actions included lengthening the assignments of manned-aircraft pilots in RPA squadrons and then extending those assignments indefinitely, mobilizing pilots from the Air National Guard and Air Force Reserve, delaying the establishment of the RPA weapons school after designating RPA as a formal weapon system, and extending the length of deployments to augment staffing levels of RPA squadrons. In 2009, the Air Force also began assigning manned-aircraft training graduates to RPA assignments as their first assignment after completing Undergraduate Pilot Training. In 2010, the Air Force established the RPA pilot career field. Figure 3 summarizes the steps that the Air Force took to react to increased CAP requirements since 2007.

Using these steps, the Air Force has made progress towards meeting the CAP requirements, but at personnel levels that were below requirements. In addition, the Air Force reduced the capacity of its RPA training unit because instructors were pulled to fly in RPA units. In fiscal year 2012, the Air Force began a reconstitution period intended to staff the training units, restart the weapons school, and increase the overall number of RPA pilots to increase the crew ratios of RPA units. As of December 2013, there were 1,366 RPA pilots, or around 85 percent of the total of 1,600 pilots determined by the Air Force as necessary to sustain RPA operations and training for 65 CAPs. In addition, the Air Force anticipates increasing the number of RPA pilot staff positions across the Air Force from 111 as of December 2013 to 300 by fiscal year 2023 to serve at various Air Force commands, including at Headquarters Air Force and Air Combat Command.

Air Force Has Not Accurately Identified Optimum Personnel Requirements and Has Not Established a Minimum Personnel Requirement

The Air Force has not accurately identified optimum personnel requirements, or crew ratio, for the number of RPA pilots it requires. We have reported that high-performing organizations use complete and current data to inform their strategic human-capital planning and remain open to reevaluating workforce planning efforts.[18] In the 2008 study that the Air Force Manpower Agency conducted to determine the appropriate crew ratios for MQ-1 Predator squadrons, the Air Force did not account for all of the flying and administrative tasks that are required in these squadrons. While the study accounted for some important tasks that RPA pilots perform in MQ-1 squadrons such as performing operational missions, it did not account for other important tasks such as those required to launch and recover RPAs. In addition, the study did not account for some important administrative tasks such as conducting flight-safety evaluations and providing a commander's support staff. The study acknowledged that due to its reporting time frames, it did not capture the personnel requirements of a variety of tasks.

Headquarters Air Force personnel acknowledged the study's limitations and said that because the study omitted critical and important tasks from its analysis, the resulting crew ratio that it recommended probably did not provide enough pilots to perform the work in an MQ-1 squadron. These officials stated that, because of the study's omissions, the 10:1 crew ratio for MQ-1 squadrons established in an Air Force instruction that was based on this study should probably be increased.[19] Similarly, some RPA unit commanders and RPA pilots in some of our focus groups also said that the crew ratio is too low.[20] However, to-date the Air Force has not updated the crew ratio for RPA squadrons. Headquarters Air Force officials stated that updating the crew ratio has not been a top priority. At the same time, these officials noted that more recently they have discussed the need to update the crew ratio and expressed optimism that it would become a priority in the future, though no concrete plans exist to initiate an update to the requirement.[21]

Furthermore, an Air Force instruction states that a crew ratio establishes the number of personnel required to support a unit mission and that if a ratio is too low, combat capability is diminished and flight safety suffers.[22] Such risks can arise when crew-ratio requirements are set too low, as well as when units operate at crew ratios that are too far below optimum crew ratios. However, Air Force documentation shows that crew ratios in RPA units have fluctuated between 7:1 and 8.5:1, and at times have dropped to 6:1, according to Air Force officials. This indicates that the RPA pilot workload is performed by fewer pilots working more hours to accomplish the mission than if the Air Force ensured that its RPA units operated at the required crew ratios. The Air Force has operated at these levels to provide a higher number of CAPs.

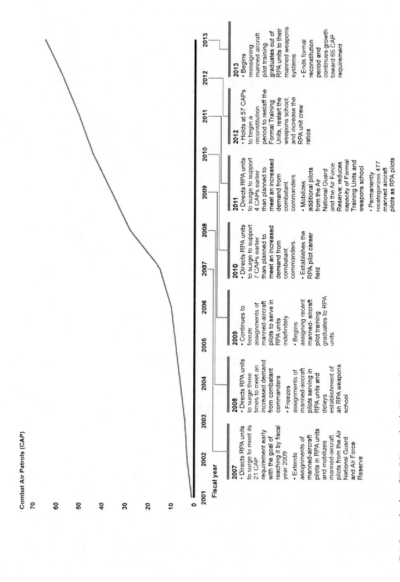

Source: GAO analysis of DOD and Air Force Documents.

Figure 3. Air Force Steps to React to Growth in Demand for Remotely Piloted Aircraft (RPA).

According to Headquarters Air Force officials, in the past the Air Force has attempted to deny requests made by combatant commanders for Air Force RPA capabilities because they push crew ratios too low. These officials stated that when the Air Force denies a request it provides justification, which include concerns about crew ratios, to the Joint Staff, which is responsible for resolving differences between combatant commanders' requests for capabilities and the services that provide them. However, Air Force officials stated that the Joint Staff has overridden some of the Air Force denials in order to accomplish missions, despite the possibility that crew ratios would decrease. Without establishing a minimum crew ratio for RPA units, the Air Force does not have the information it needs to determine when those units are operating at crew ratio levels that expose the Air Force to unacceptable levels of risk to accomplishing its mission and ensuring safety.

A High Pace of Operations and Work Demands Limit Time for Training and Development

As a result of inaccurate crew ratios for Air Force RPA squadrons and a lack of a minimum crew ratio, the RPA pilot workforce has sustained a high pace of operations, which limits its time for training and development. The Air Force Unmanned Aircraft Systems Flight Plan 2009-2047 states that it is imperative to provide the necessary training and opportunities for advancement that will create a cadre of future Air Force leaders.[23] However, unit commanders in each of the three locations we visited and some RPA pilots stated that the high pace of operations and demand for RPA capabilities limited their units' time to train for the various mission sets that RPA units are required to perform.[24] One unit commander stated that battlefield commanders that his unit supports have pointed out that his RPA pilots need training, and pilots in some focus groups noted that limited training opportunities prevent RPA units from excelling at their missions and becoming experts in their field. In addition, pilots in all 10 focus groups indicated that they are limited in their ability to pursue developmental opportunities.[25]

Furthermore, DOD has noted that the prevalence and use of unmanned systems, including RPAs, will continue to grow at a dramatic pace. As discussed above, the Secretary of Defense has stated specifically that the requirement for 65 CAPs represents a temporary plateau in progress toward an increased enduring requirement. Also, as the national security environment changes, RPA pilots will be expected to conduct a broader range of missions across different conditions and environments, including antiaccess and area-denial environments where the freedom to operate RPAs is contested.[26] By not creating an environment where RPA pilots can receive the training and development opportunities they need to perform their functions effectively, the Air Force may be hindering its ability to perform its mission even if it is able to operate at the optimum crew ratio that is set in the Air Force instruction.

The Air Force Faces Challenges Recruiting RPA Pilots and May Face Challenges Retaining Them in the Future

The Air Force has used a dual strategy to meet its increasing need for RPA pilots: using manned-aircraft pilots and recruiting RPA pilots, the career field established in 2010 for officers trained to only fly RPAs. However, the Air Force has faced challenges in recruiting RPA pilots since it began this career field. High-performing organizations tailor their recruitment and retention strategies to meet their specific mission needs.[27] The Air Force intends to build a cadre of dedicated RPA pilots, and projects that RPA pilots will make up 90 percent of the RPA pilot workforce by fiscal year 2022. However, the Air Force has not been able to achieve its recruiting goals for RPA pilots in fiscal years 2012 and 2013. In fiscal year 2013, the Air Force recruited 110 new RPA pilots, missing its goal of 179 pilots by around 39 percent. Consequently, while the Air Force has made progress in increasing the total number of RPA pilots and staffed its RPA units at about 85 percent of current requirements as of December 2013, around 42 percent of those pilots are manned-aircraft pilots and manned-aircraft pilot training graduates. Both of these groups are temporary RPA pilots who serve only one assignment in an RPA squadron. While the length of these assignments can be extended, these pilots will likely not stay in the RPA squadrons permanently (see figure 4).

Headquarters Air Force officials believe the Air Force has missed its recruiting goals in 2012 and 2013 for RPA pilots because potential recruits have a limited understanding of the RPA mission and there is a lack of recruiting officials with RPA experience to advise potential recruits. The Air Force may face challenges recruiting officers to serve as RPA pilots because of a negative perception that some in the Air Force associate with flying RPAs. Headquarters Air Force officials, RPA pilots in some of our focus groups, and one unit commander stated that some in the Air Force view flying RPAs negatively, resulting in a stigma.

According to these officials one reason some view flying an RPA negatively is because flying an RPA does not require pilots to operate an aircraft while on board an aircraft in-flight. In addition, officials stated that overcoming this stigma may be difficult because publicizing the work that RPA pilots do is often not feasible due to the classified nature of RPA missions. Nonetheless, Headquarters Air Force officials stated that the Air Force projects it will meet its recruiting goals for the RPA pilot career field for fiscal year 2014 on the basis of commitments made by cadets participating in the Air Force Reserve Officer Training Corps.

We have reported that high-performing organizations make use of targeted investments such as recruiting bonuses as part of their strategies to recruit high-quality personnel with the critical skills. However, Headquarters Air Force officials reported that the Air Force is not currently exercising its option to offer a recruiting bonus as an incentive to volunteer for the RPA pilot career field. Officials from the Headquarters Air Force and the Office of the Secretary of Defense stated that such pay incentives are rarely used to recruit officers in the Air Force. Headquarters Air Force officials also stated that due to the current constrained budget environment in which DOD and the federal government are operating, the Air Force would first prefer to exhaust the use of all nonmonetary options for improving recruiting before offering bonuses. As a result, the Air Force may have to continue to rely on manned-aircraft pilots to meet RPA pilot personnel needs. This approach may not be cost-effective because the Air Force spends an average of $557,000 per pilot on traditional Undergraduate Pilot Training, compared to an average of $65,000 for Undergraduate RPA Training, according to Air Education and Training Command officials. Without a more-tailored approach to recruiting RPA pilots that increases the appeal of the new career to potential recruits, the Air Force risks perpetuating personnel shortages and may need to continue relying on manned-aircraft pilots to fill its personnel requirements.

Moreover, the Air Force uses officers as RPA pilots, but it has not evaluated whether using alternative personnel populations such as enlisted or civilian personnel as RPA pilots is a viable option. A report by the House Permanent Select Committee on Intelligence urged the Air Force to study the other military services' experiences with using enlisted personnel as RPA operators and evaluate whether this approach would degrade mission performance.[28] Headquarters Air Force officials stated that prior to 2010, they decided to assign officers to serve as RPA pilots because they thought officers were more appropriate since RPAs fly in complex airspace, and, in some cases, fire missiles at adversaries. Headquarters Air Force officials also stated that they have, at times, considered the use of enlisted or civilian personnel but have not initiated formal efforts to evaluate whether using such populations would negatively affect the ability of the Air Force to carry out its missions. However, without an evaluation of the viability of using other sources of personnel, the Air Force may lack valuable information on whether additional options exist for meeting personnel requirements.

With regard to pilot retention, the Air Force has taken some steps but does not have a retention strategy for RPA pilots, though indications suggest that it could face challenges retaining them in the future. Specifically, according to Headquarters Air Force officials, the Air Force has offered assignment incentive payments to RPA pilots since the career field was established in 2010. In addition, the officials stated that manned- aircraft pilots serving assignments in RPA squadrons receive skill-based aviator career incentive pay and can receive aviator retention pay by extending their service commitment in the Air Force. Despite these incentive payments, pilots in 7 of 10 focus groups we conducted indicated that retention of RPA pilots is or will be a challenge. In addition, pilots in some focus groups stated that they are considering their options for leaving active-duty service in the Air Force to go to the Air National Guard, or Air Force Reserve, or the private sector. Unit commanders in one location we visited, pilots in some of our focus groups, and other Air Force officials stated that they were concerned about the future retention rates of RPA pilots.

Headquarters Air Force officials stated that the Air Force's strategy for meeting personnel requirements has focused on recruiting and that they have not observed indications of a concern with the retention of RPA pilots. However, the Air Force has not evaluated the potential effect of the difficult working conditions, such as long working hours and frequently rotating shifts that we discuss in more detail later in this report, that RPA pilots face and how those conditions may affect the Air Force's ability to retain RPA pilots, despite the situation that many of these pilots will begin to reach the end of their service commitments in fiscal year 2017. In a 2011 memorandum to the Air Force, the Secretary of Defense directed the Air Force to provide sufficient incentives to retain high-quality RPA personnel. Although the Air Force has made retention payments available to RPA pilots, these efforts may not be enough or appropriate to overcome the challenges the Air Force may face to retain RPA pilots.

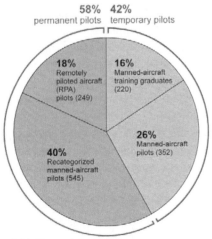

Source: GAO analysis of Air Force data.

Figure 4. Distribution of Permanent and Temporary Air Force Pilots of Remotely Piloted Aircraft (RPA).

The Air Force Has Mechanisms to Collect Feedback from RPA Pilots but Has Not Used That Feedback to Manage Its Human-Capital Strategy for RPA Pilots

While the Air Force has mechanisms in place to collect feedback from RPA pilots, it has not used this feedback to develop its strategic human-capital approach to managing RPA pilots, such as by incorporating their feedback into tailoring a recruiting and retention strategy or by taking actions related to training and development. High-performing organizations involve their employees in their strategic human-capital approaches and planning in order to improve motivation and morale by seeking employee feedback on a periodic basis, and using that input to adjust their human-capital approaches.

The Air Force has mechanisms in place that it has used to collect feedback from RPA pilots. For example, the Air Force solicits feedback from RPA units as well as all other Air Force units during an annual Unit Climate Assessment that gauges discrimination, harassment, and morale issues at the unit level. While this effort is not specific to the RPA units, it does include assessments of RPA units. Unit commanders can use the results of their Unit Climate Assessments to address challenges at the local unit level. However, Headquarters Air Force officials responsible for managing RPA pilots have not obtained information from these assessments to identify whether they include potentially valuable information about any concerns related to establishing the RPA pilot career field. Headquarters Air Force officials stated that the Air Force created this career field more quickly and under greater operational demand than any career field in recent Air Force history. However, these officials also stated that using feedback from the Unit Climate Assessments to address issues at a headquarters level that would affect RPA pilots could undermine unit commanders. They also noted that officials at the headquarters level might lack the proper context for understanding the assessment results.

The Air Force also collected feedback from RPA pilots in studies the Air Force School of Aerospace Medicine published in 2011 and 2013 to assess the level of and reasons for stress in personnel assigned to RPA units, which included surveys and interviews of RPA pilots. In response to these studies, the Air Force took actions designed to address stress in personnel assigned to RPA units. For instance, the studies recommended that the Air Force assign an operational psychologist to each RPA unit, and, in response, local flight surgeons, clinical providers, and aerospace physiologists have created teams to help address stress concerns at the base level. While researchers from the Air Force's medical research community conducted these studies, they included findings related to personnel shortages that are germane to the Air Force personnel and operations communities. However, Headquarters Air Force officials from the personnel and operations communities stated that, prior to our review, they were unaware of the studies and their findings.

RPA pilots in our focus groups also noted information that suggests that incorporating pilot feedback from existing mechanisms could help improve communication and address issues pilots are facing. For example, pilots in some of our focus groups stated that they did not know what the career path for an RPA pilot is or what steps they should take to advance. Further, in some of our focus groups, manned-aircraft pilots who are serving assignments as RPA pilots expressed uncertainty regarding whether they will be able to return to their manned platforms and what effect, if any, their RPA assignment will have on their careers. Pilots in some focus groups also reported that senior leadership had not communicated to them about this uncertainty, and one pilot specifically noted that the lack of communication negatively affects morale. Without using existing mechanisms to obtain feedback from RPA pilots directly, Headquarters Air Force may be missing an opportunity to obtain information that can help it address recruiting, retention, training, and development challenges related to RPA pilots.

AIR FORCE HAS TAKEN SOME ACTIONS TO ADDRESS THE POTENTIALLY CHALLENGING WORKING CONDITIONS RPA PILOTS FACE BUT HAS NOT FULLY ANALYZED BEING DEPLOYED-ON-STATION

Air Force RPA Pilots Find Their Work Rewarding but Report Multiple Challenging Working Conditions, Some of Which the Air Force Has Taken Actions to Address

RPA pilots find their mission rewarding, but they reported that they face multiple, challenging working conditions. RPA pilots in 8 of the 10 focus groups we conducted reported that they found it rewarding to be able to contribute to combat operations every day through the RPA mission. For instance, one pilot stated that the mission is the reason that he had decided to become a permanent RPA pilot and that it was rewarding to contribute to overseas contingency operations, which he would not be able to do in any other job. Similarly, the Air Force School of Aerospace Medicine published studies in 2011 and 2013 that evaluated the psychological condition of RPA personnel and found that RPA pilots held positive perceptions of the effect and contributions of their work. However, RPA pilots also stated that they face multiple challenging working conditions including: long hours, working shifts that frequently rotate, and remaining in assignments beyond typical lengths.[29] RPA pilots in all of our focus groups reported that these challenging conditions negatively affected their morale and caused them stress. Similarly, the Air Force School of Aerospace Medicine studies found that RPA personnel reported sources of stress that were consistent with the challenges we identified. These challenges include the following:

- RPA pilots in 8 of our 10 focus groups stated, and Air Force studies we reviewed show, that RPA pilots work long hours. RPA pilots in 7 of our focus groups described factors that contribute to their long hours including performing administrative duties and attending briefings, in addition to flying shifts. The Air Force studies also found that working long hours was one of the top five reasons for stress among personnel in RPA squadrons. In the studies, over 57 percent of respondents reported that they worked more than 50 hours per week. In addition, the studies found that over 40 percent of respondents reported that performing administrative duties added hours to their work week and was the third-highest reason for stress among active-duty RPA personnel.

- RPA pilots also reported that it was challenging to work on shifts that rotate. RPA pilots in 7 of the 10 focus groups we conducted stated that constantly rotating shifts caused sleep problems for them because they must continuously adjust their sleep schedule to accommodate new shifts.[30] In addition, pilots noted that continuously rotating to new shifts disrupted their ability to spend time with their family and friends. Officials told us that it was ideal for pilots working evening or night shifts to maintain a consistent sleep pattern on their off-duty days even though those sleep patterns would require that pilots sleep while their family and friends were awake. However, some RPA pilots reported that they typically adjusted their sleep schedules dramatically on their off-duty days so they could spend time with their families and that these changes to their sleep schedules resulted in significant fatigue both at home and when they returned to work. Similarly, over half of the respondents to the surveys included in the Air Force studies we reviewed reported that shift work caused a moderate to large amount of their stress.

- RPA pilots in 5 of our focus groups reported that being assigned to continue flying RPAs for periods extending beyond the typical Air Force assignment was difficult. In all of the focus groups we conducted with RPA pilots, those who plan to return to flying manned aircraft stated that they have been required to stay in their assignments for periods that are longer than a typical Air Force assignment. Air Force officials stated that there is no requirement for officers to move to a new assignment after a specified period. However, pilots in our focus groups and Air Force headquarters officials said that officer assignments typically last 3 to 4 years. Air Force documentation shows that some of these pilots have been in their RPA assignments for over 6 years. Moreover, the Air Force studies also found that one of the most common stressors that RPA personnel cited was the lack of clarity regarding when they would return to their careers in manned aircraft. Specifically, the 2011 study states that the Air Force informed RPA pilots who previously flew manned aircraft that their RPA assignments were temporary and after 3 to 4 years they could return to their manned-aircraft career.[31] The study goes on to state that due to the increasing demand for RPAs and the long-standing surge in RPA operations, many pilots have been unable to return to their manned-aircraft careers and, until recently, the Air Force kept them in these assignments indefinitely.

The Air Force has taken some actions to address some of the challenging working conditions that RPA pilots face. The Air Force studies included over 10 recommendations to address the sources of stress that RPA personnel reported. For example, the studies recommended that the Air Force assign an operational psychologist to each RPA unit to help commanders optimize work-rest schedules and shift cycles, and identify pilots who are reaching elevated levels of fatigue or stress. In response, the Air Force has assigned mental-health providers that are dedicated to RPA squadrons at Beale, Cannon, and Creech Air Force Bases. However, the studies also recommended that the Air Force increase staffing in RPA squadrons to reduce the number of hours that RPA personnel work and to help establish better shift schedules. Air Force researchers stated that increasing staffing levels, or crew ratios, in RPA squadrons would be the most-effective means to reduce RPA pilot stress, but as discussed above, the Air Force has operated its RPA squadrons below the optimum crew ratios.

Air Force Has Not Fully Analyzed Challenges That RPA Pilots Face Related to Being Deployed-on- Station

RPA pilots also face challenges related to being deployed-on-station as they balance their warfighting responsibilities with their personal lives. Because pilots are able to operate RPAs from Air Force bases in the United States and are thus able to live at home—what is known as being deployed-on-station—their dual role juxtaposes stress related to supporting combat operations with the strains that can occur in their personal lives. While these pilots face this challenging working condition that may affect their quality of life, DOD's *Quadrennial Quality of Life Reviews* have emphasized DOD's continued commitment to provide servicemembers with the best quality of life possible.[32]

Being deployed-on-station is a new concept in warfighting, and a 2011 report[33] prepared for the Air Force Medical Support Agency describes five conditions that personnel who are deployed-on-station can experience. The report notes that these personnel (1) experience a justifiable risk of being the target of hostile adversary attacks because they are combatants and their bank accounts, reputations, or physical safety could be targeted; (2) operate in contact with and sometimes kill adversaries, although operations they conduct are out of direct risk from combat; (3) must act with urgency to sometimes kill adversaries and take other time- pressured actions to help ensure combatants they support do not lose their lives; (4) work on a wartime rhythm that includes 24/7 operations 365 days a year; and (5) are required to conceal information from friends and family about their work because their missions are often classified. A Headquarters Air Force official described being deployed-on-station as a status between deployed-in-theater and not deployed and emphasized that personnel who are deployed-on-station are not directly engaged in combat, which is a significant component of being deployed. The official also acknowledged that being deployed-on-station can be more challenging than assignments with more-limited connections to the battlefield.

RPA pilots in each of the 10 focus groups we conducted reported that being deployed-on-station negatively affected their quality of life, as it was challenging for them to balance their warfighting responsibilities with their personal lives for extended periods of time. RPA pilots in some of our focus groups, as well as commanders of RPA squadrons, noted that they would prefer to deploy-in-theater for 6 months with a clear end point and be separated from their family and friends rather than be deployed-on- station for 3 or more years. One commander stated that he preferred being deployed-in-theater and knowing when his deployment would end. In contrast, he stated that in an RPA squadron, it was difficult to juggle his warfighting role with the typical challenges of home life for multiple years. Likewise, the Air Force studies found that being deployed-on-station was one of the most commonly cited stressors that RPA personnel reported.[34]

In addition, RPA pilots in 6 of our 10 focus groups reported that they are expected to do more work than their counterparts who are deployed-in-theater. For example, RPA pilots in some of our focus groups who had previously deployed-in-theater stated that they are expected to complete administrative tasks that are not required of them when they are deployed-in-theater.

Headquarters Air Force officials as well as pilots in some of our focus groups stated that the Air Force provides support to personnel who are deployed-in-theater that it does not provide for personnel who are deployed-on-station. Moreover, the Air Force has surveyed RPA personnel and other deployed-on-station personnel to study their stress and mental health, but it has not fully analyzed the effects of being deployed-on-station. Specifically, it has not fully analyzed whether being deployed-on-station has negative effects on quality of life that are not attributable to the stressors that are related to low unit-staffing levels that we discussed above such as rotating shifts and long assignments. As a result, the Air Force does not have the information it needs to determine whether being deployed-on-station has a negative effect on the quality of life of RPA pilots that is not attributed to the other factors and what steps might be needed to reduce those effects.

THE AIR FORCE MONITORS RPA PILOT PROMOTION RATES BUT HAS NOT ANALYZED FACTORS RELATED TO THOSE RATES

The Air Force Monitors RPA Pilot Promotion Rates and Has Found That They Are Lower Than in Other Career Fields

AFPC monitors the promotion rates of RPA pilots and has found that they were promoted below the average rate for active-duty line officers on 20 of 24 officer promotion boards since 2006. We reached the same conclusion based on our review of data for these promotion boards. We also found that RPA pilots were promoted below the average rate of manned-aircraft pilots[35] on 21 of 24 boards. Furthermore, we compared the promotion rates of RPA pilots to those of other career fields and found that RPA pilots were promoted at the lowest rate of any career field on 9 of the 24 boards and were promoted in the lowest 5 percent of the career fields that competed on 5 additional boards.[36] Conversely, RPA pilots were promoted in the top 50 percent of the career fields that competed on only 3 boards of the 24 boards. More specifically, RPA pilots competing for promotion to each rank that we analyzed faced challenges. RPA pilots competing for promotion to major were promoted in the top 50 percent on just one of the seven promotion boards since 2006. RPA pilots competing for promotion to lieutenant colonel were promoted at the lowest or next-to-lowest rate compared to the other career fields that competed on 7 of the 9 boards since 2006. Likewise, RPA pilots competing for promotion to the rank of colonel had the lowest promotion rate of any career field that competed on 4 of the 8 colonel boards since 2006. Figures 5, 6, and 7 display the results of our analyses.

Air Force Has Not Analyzed Factors Related to Lower RPA Pilot Promotion Rates

While AFPC has monitored the promotion rates of RPA pilots, it has not analyzed the factors related to lower promotion rates for these pilots. It is a common statistical practice when analyzing how selected factors are related to a given outcome to account for other key factors that could also be related to the outcome. Although AFPC analyzed the promotions of officers in the Line of the Air Force competitive category, which includes RPA pilots, and identified factors related to promotion outcomes for officers in this category, it has not incorporated a key factor—the career field effect of being an RPA pilot—into its analysis.

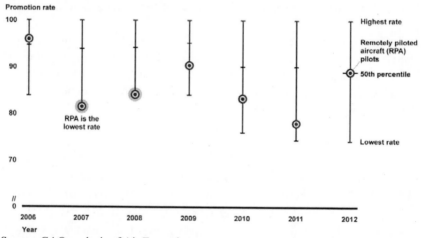

Source: GAO analysis of Air Force data.

Note: The Air Force did not hold a promotion board for Line of the Air Force majors in 2013. At least 10 eligible officers from between 29 and 33 careers competed, in the zone, for promotion to the rank of major in the Line of the Air Force competitive category between 2006 and 2012.

Figure 5. The Rates of Promotion to Major for Pilots of Remotely Piloted Aircraft (RPA) Compared to Other Air Force Officer Careers, 2006 to 2012.

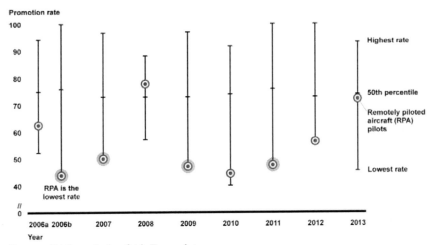

Source: GAO analysis of Air Force data.

Note: The Air Force held two promotion boards in 2006 for Line of the Air Force lieutenant colonels. Fewer than 10 RPA pilots were eligible for the 2006a, 2007, and 2008 promotion boards. At least 10 eligible officers from between 26 and 30 careers competed, in-the-zone, for promotion to the rank of lieutenant colonel in the Line of the Air Force competitive category between 2006 and 2013.

Figure 6. The Rates of Promotion to Lieutenant Colonel for Pilots of Remotely Piloted Aircraft (RPA) Compared to Other Air Force Officer Careers, 2006 to 2013.

AFPC analyzed promotion data of officers in the competitive category that includes RPA pilots called Line of the Air Force and found multiple factors related to promotion outcomes. Specifically, AFPC analyzed these data using logistic regression, which is a statistical method that enables AFPC to analyze the relationships among multiple factors. Using this method, AFPC identified a number of factors that are positively and negatively related to promotions. For example, AFPC found that one of the two factors with the most-substantial positive relationship to promotions was for an officer to have completed a professional military education program by attending an Air Force school in-residence, rather than completing the same professional military education program by correspondence. The other factor with the most-substantial positive relationship was for an officer to have completed an advanced academic degree. By contrast, AFPC found that officers who have unfavorable information, such as performance-related reprimands, in their personnel files are promoted at lower rates, in general, than officers who do not.

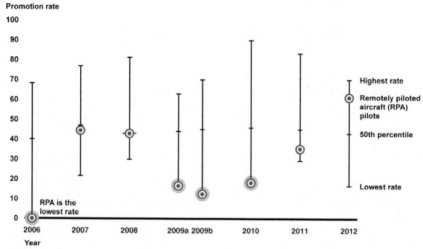

Source: GAO analysis of Air Force data.

Note: The Air Force held two promotion boards for Line of the Air Force colonels in 2009. Also, the Air Force held a promotion board for Line of the Air Force colonels in November 2013, but the results were not available as of February 2014. Fewer than 10 RPA pilots were eligible for the 2006, 2007, 2008, 2009a, and 2009b promotion boards. At least 10 eligible officers from between 22 and 26 careers competed, in-the-zone, for promotion to the rank of colonel in the Line of the Air Force competitive category between 2006 and 2012.

Figure 7. The Rates of Promotion Rates to Colonel for Pilots of Remotely Piloted Aircraft (RPA) Compared to Other Air Force Officer Careers, 2006 to 2012.

AFPC did not include the career field effect of being an RPA pilot as a factor in its analysis. As a result, AFPC does not know whether or how being an RPA pilot is related to promotions for these pilots. AFPC has analyzed other careers and found that most careers are not related to promotion rates. AFPC officials stated that they had not analyzed this effect because most of the officers currently serving as RPA pilots are temporary RPA pilots and AFPC does not typically analyze a career field effect of temporary assignments.

In addition, AFPC assumed that the factors that were substantially related to promotions for the Line of the Air Force category were also substantially related to promotions for the RPA pilot subgroup, but did not confirm that its assumption was warranted. AFPC officials stated that when they analyzed the records of RPA pilots, they focused on the factors identified in the analysis of Line of the Air Force officers, including completing professional military education in-residence and advanced degrees. They found that RPA pilots generally completed professional military education in-residence and advanced degrees at lower rates compared to the average rates for officers who had been promoted since 2006. However, by not including the career field effect of being an RPA pilot into its analysis, the Air Force cannot determine whether these factors have the same relationship with RPA pilot promotions as they do on officer promotions in the broader Line of the Air Force category.

Air Force Reported Reasons for Low RPA Pilot Promotions Rates to Congress and Took Actions in Response without a Comprehensive Understanding

The Air Force reported reasons for low RPA pilot promotions rates to Congress and took actions to raise those rates without a comprehensive understanding of the factors related to the promotion rates of these pilots. Specifically, the Air Force attributed low RPA pilot promotion rates to three factors: (1) RPA pilots completed professional military education at lower rates than average; (2) RPA pilots completed advanced degrees at lower rates than average; and (3) the process the Air Force used to select RPA pilots. As discussed above, the AFPC's approach to identify the first two factors assumed that their relationships with promotion rates for RPA pilots as a subgroup would be the same as those with the Line of the Air Force as a whole, but this assumption was not confirmed through analysis. Regarding the third factor, Air Force documentation states "lower quality pilots are generally sent to RPA squadrons."[37]

Headquarters Air Force officials and two commanders of manned-aircraft squadrons explained that commanders select pilots from their squadrons to assign to RPA squadrons and in general most commanders assign less-skilled pilots and less-competent officers to these squadrons. Headquarters officials also stated that less-skilled and less-competent officers generally had fewer of the factors AFPC identified that positively influence promotions in their records than their peers. Air Force officials also explained that because the bulk of RPA pilots who have competed for promotion since 2006 were assigned using this process, they believe these are the reasons that RPA pilots have been promoted at lower rates than their peers. However, the Air Force has not incorporated variables into its analysis to account for RPA pilots or the process to assign them to determine whether they are related to promotions of RPA pilots. Consequently, the Air Force report to Congress may not be accurate because the Air Force does not have comprehensive analysis to demonstrate that these factors are actually related to RPA pilot promotions.

Recently, the Air Force has taken actions to raise promotion rates of RPA pilots. First, to communicate to promotion boards that promoting RPA pilots was important, the Secretary of the Air Force has issued instructions since 2008 to each officer promotion board, directing them to consider the strategic effect made by RPA pilots when evaluating their records for promotion. In the instructions, the Secretary directs board members to consider that RPA pilots' records may not show the same career progression as their peers because of operational requirements they have had to meet to satisfy the needs of the Air Force. Second, the Air Force intervened on behalf of RPA pilots to enhance their opportunities to achieve one of the two most important factors that AFPC identified in its analysis of all Line of the Air Force officers by reserving 46 in-residence seats in Air Force professional military education schools in 2012 for RPA pilots who were competing to be promoted to major. Moreover, the Air Force stated in its August 2013 report to Congress that its long-term plan to raise promotion rates is to attract "quality" recruits to the RPA pilot career field and to establish a sustainable pace of operations that will enable these pilots time to complete in-residence professional military education and advanced academic degrees. However, because it has not fully analyzed the career field effects of being an RPA pilot, it is unclear whether the Air Force is targeting these corrective actions at the right factors. Consequently, the Air Force's actions may have limited effect on improving the promotion rates for RPA pilots.

CONCLUSION

The Air Force has demonstrated a commitment in recent years to the use of RPAs, believing that the capabilities they provide are worth the service's investment in both platforms and personnel. As the RPA pilot career field evolves, it will be important that Air Force senior leadership demonstrates a commitment to a human-capital management approach that addresses a number of outstanding challenges. For instance, without updating its optimum crew ratio for RPA units, the Air Force may have RPA pilot shortfalls even after its current requirement is met, which could exacerbate existing strains on this workforce. In addition, by not establishing a minimum crew ratio below which RPA units cannot operate, the Air Force does not know when it is operating at unacceptable levels of risk to mission and safety. Further, without developing a strategy tailored to address specific challenges of recruiting and retaining RPA pilots, current pilot shortfalls may persist even longer than expected. Finally, without evaluating the viability of using alternative personnel populations, such as enlisted or civilian personnel, the Air Force may not meet and sustain required RPA pilot staffing levels.

Moreover, without incorporating feedback from RPA pilots using existing feedback mechanisms, the Air Force may be missing opportunities to manage its human-capital strategies effectively for these pilots. Also, RPA pilots face a number of challenging working conditions that can affect their quality of life including those associated with being deployed-on- station. However, without analyzing whether being deployed-on-station has long-term negative effects, the Air Force does not have the information it needs to determine whether it should take any action in response. Finally, while the Air Force has taken action to improve the chances for RPA pilots to be promoted, senior Air Force leaders cannot be assured that the actions are the appropriate ones because the Air Force has not analyzed the effect that being an RPA pilot itself may have on those chances.

RECOMMENDATIONS FOR EXECUTIVE ACTION

We recommend that the Secretary of Defense direct the Secretary of the Air Force to take the following seven actions:

- update crew ratios for RPA units to help ensure that the Air Force establishes a more-accurate understanding of the required number of RPA pilots needed in its units,
- establish a minimum crew ratio in Air Force policy below which RPA units cannot operate without running unacceptable levels of risk to accomplishing the mission and ensuring safety,
- develop a recruiting and retention strategy that is a tailored to the specific needs and challenges of RPA pilots to help ensure that the Air Force can meet and retain required staffing levels to meet its mission,
- evaluate the viability of using alternative personnel populations including enlisted or civilian personnel as RPA pilots to identify whether such populations could help the Air Force meet and sustain required RPA pilot staffing levels,
- incorporate feedback from RPA pilots by using existing mechanisms or by collecting direct feedback from RPA pilots,

- analyze the effects of being deployed-on-station to determine whether there are resulting negative effects on the quality of life of RPA pilots and take responsive actions as appropriate, and
- include the career field effect of being an RPA pilot into AFPC's analysis to determine whether and how being an RPA pilot is related to promotions and determine whether the factors AFPC identified in its analysis of Line of the Air Force officers are also related to RPA pilot promotions.

AGENCY COMMENTS AND OUR EVALUATION

We provided a draft of this report to DOD for review and comment. The Deputy Director of Force Management Policy, Headquarters Air Force provided written comments in response to our report. In its written comments, the Air Force concurred with four of our seven recommendations and partially concurred with the remaining three recommendations. The Air Force also provided technical comments that we have incorporated into this report where applicable.

In concurring with our first three recommendations, the Air Force stated that it:

- has an effort underway to update crew ratios for RPA units and expects to have this effort completed by February 2015;
- a minimum crew ratio would indicate when the Air Force receives a request for forces that would pose risks to the mission and safety and it expects to respond to our recommendation by February 2015; and
- will develop a recruiting and retention strategy that is tailored to the specific needs and challenges of RPA pilots and expects to have this done by October 2015.

In concurring with our fifth recommendation, to incorporate feedback from RPA pilots by using existing mechanisms or by collecting direct feedback from RPA pilots, the Air Force stated that if it determines that it is appropriate to collect such feedback, it will do so using a survey. We continue to believe that collecting this feedback could be a useful tool for the Air Force to develop a tailored recruiting and retention strategy and to inform actions it may take related to training and developing RPA pilots.

The Air Force partially concurred with our fourth recommendation that it evaluate the viability of using alternative personnel populations as RPA pilots and determine if such populations could help the Air Force meet and sustain required RPA pilot staffing levels. The Air Force stated that it considered assigning enlisted personnel as RPA pilots, but it decided that the responsibilities of piloting an RPA were commensurate with the rank of officers instead. At the same time, the Air Force stated that it has initiated a review of some of its missions and the ranks needed to execute those missions and that it may consider using enlisted airmen in this review.

In our report, we acknowledge that the Air Force had previously considered using enlisted personnel as RPA pilots and that the Air Force decided instead to use officers. However, it is not clear what steps the Air Force took in its previous considerations. We think it is a positive step that the Air Force has initiated a review of Air Force missions and rank requirements to execute those missions. Considering the significant role that RPAs play in the Air Force mission, we believe the Air Force should include RPA pilots in its review to evaluate whether enlisted personnel as well as civilians may provide a means for the Air Force to address shortfalls in the staffing levels of RPA pilots.

In addition, the Air Force partially concurred with our sixth recommendation that it analyze the effects of being deployed-on-station to determine if there are resulting negative effects on RPA pilots' quality of life and take responsive actions as appropriate. In response to our recommendation, the Air Force stated that it had studied the effects that being deployed-on-station has on RPA pilots and that many of the stressors it identified in these studies were related to low unit staffing levels. In addition, the Air Force asked us to focus our recommendation on an evaluation of these studies.

We acknowledge in our report that the Air Force evaluated the psychological condition of RPA personnel who are deployed-on-station in studies it published in 2011 and 2013. We also acknowledge that the primary recommendation these studies make is to increase staffing levels in RPA units to alleviate the stress of RPA personnel. As we discussed in our report, RPA units have been understaffed and thus increasing staffing levels may be appropriate. However, our finding is focused on whether being deployed-on-station has negative effects on quality of life that are not attributable to the stressors that are related to low unit-staffing levels. We think that a more complete understanding of the effects of being deployed-on-station that are not attributable to low staffing levels will help the Air Force determine if responsive actions are needed that go beyond increasing staffing levels. Further, the 2011 report prepared for the Air Force Medical Support Agency that focuses more directly on the concept of being deployed-on-station is a constructive source of input for the Air Force to understand any negative effects of being deployed-on-station. However, it is not clear that an evaluation of this report and the 2011 and 2013 studies will provide the Air Force with a complete understanding of this new deployment concept's consequences for its personnel.

Finally, the Air Force partially concurred with our seventh recommendation that it include the career field effect of being an RPA pilot into AFPC's promotion analysis to determine if being an RPA pilot is related to promotions and determine if other factors that AFPC identified in its analysis of Line of the Air Force officers are also related to RPA pilot promotions. The Air Force stated that the RPA career field is a subsection of the Line of the Air Force and therefore factors related to promotions identified in analysis of the Line of the Air Force are directly related to RPA pilot promotions. In our report, we acknowledge that the Air Force identified factors related to promotion outcomes for officers in the Line of the Air Force competitive category. However, as we discussed in the report, not including the career field effect of being an RPA pilot as a factor in its analysis has several consequences. First, AFPC does not know whether or how being an RPA pilot is related to promotions for these pilots. Second, the Air Force cannot determine whether the factors that it found that are related to promotions for the Line of the Air Force competitive category have the same relationship with RPA pilot promotions. Third, the information the Air Force included in a report to Congress in August 2013 on education, training, and promotion rates of RPA pilots may not be accurate. Finally, it is unclear whether the Air Force is targeting actions to increase RPA promotion rates at the right factors and thus its actions may have limited effect.

Brenda S. Farrell
Director, Defense Capabilities and Management

APPENDIX I. SCOPE AND METHODOLOGY

To understand the context of each of the issues in our review, we analyzed various Department of Defense (DOD) and Air Force documents. This documentation included a report[38] to Congress by the Office of the Under

Secretary of Defense for Acquisition, Technology and Logistics on the future of unmanned aerial systems and a report[39] by the Air Force Audit Agency on the Air Force's personnel management of pilots flying RPAs. We also reviewed reports that we previously issued that address topics related to our review including a 2010 report on DOD planning, training, and doctrine for unmanned aircraft systems.[40]

To evaluate the extent to which the Air Force uses a strategic human-capital approach to manage remotely piloted aircraft (RPA) pilots, we used a model of human-capital management GAO had previously developed[41] that specifies leading practices that high-performing organizations exhibit in their strategic human-capital management. The Model for Strategic Human Capital Management is intended to help federal organizations use their human capital effectively and integrate human-capital considerations into daily decision making and planning for the program results they wish to accomplish. It identifies concepts and leading practices that are organized into strategic human-capital management cornerstones including strategic human-capital planning; acquiring, developing, and retaining talent; and creating results-oriented cultures.

To adapt the criteria to the context of this review, we reviewed the model to identify specific practices that organizations can use to make progress associated with each of the four strategic human-capital management cornerstones. We then analyzed each practice to determine whether it was appropriate and relevant to both the RPA pilot workforce and the military context overall. After identifying the list of practices, we discussed our adaptation with Air Force officials, who agreed they were appropriate and relevant and provided points of contact for obtaining information on each practice.

We interviewed officials from Headquarters Air Force offices including the Officer of Manpower, Personnel, and Services Policy and the Office of Operations, Plans, and Requirements Policy to gather their perspectives and information on practices across all four cornerstones. From these offices, we obtained and analyzed documentation, including strategic DOD and Air Force guidance and data on personnel levels, recruiting, incentive pays, and attrition rates for remotely piloted aircraft (RPA) pilots. In addition, we interviewed knowledgeable officials from the Office of the Under Secretary of Defense for Military Personnel Policy on the Air Force's use of incentives to recruit and retain RPA pilots. We collected perspectives from RPA pilots and RPA unit commanders on the Air Force's strategic human-capital planning practices, including the effects of those practices on their training, professional development, quality of life, and retention, as well as any efforts the Air Force has made to solicit feedback from and communicate about key issues with RPA pilots. We also interviewed knowledgeable officials from the Air Force Personnel Center on practices related to results-oriented cultures.

Furthermore, we compared the perspectives and documentation we collected to the GAO criteria and held discussions with Air Force officials to discuss instances in which the Air Force's management actions were not consistent with these criteria. We discussed challenges raised by the RPA pilots and unit commanders with whom we spoke, including any efforts in place to address the challenges.

To evaluate the extent to which the Air Force has addressed concerns, if any, about the working conditions of RPA pilots that may affect their quality of life, we identified and analyzed criteria included in DOD's 2009 and 2004 *Quadrennial Quality of Life Reviews* in which DOD expresses its commitment to provide servicemembers with the best quality of life possible through support and development of responses to emerging servicemember needs. DOD has broadly defined quality of life to include such factors as morale, health and wellness, and work-life balance. To understand these reviews and the commitments, we obtained information from the Office of the Deputy Assistant Secretary of Defense for Military Community & Family Policy, which is responsible for conducting the department's *Quadrennial Quality of Life Reviews*. To understand challenges in the working conditions that RPA pilots may face we analyzed studies that the Air Force conducted to assess the stress and mental-health condition of RPA personnel, including RPA pilots.

In particular, we reviewed and analyzed two studies conducted by the Air Force School of Aerospace Medicine published in 2011 and 2013, which identified the sources of stress of RPA personnel.[42] The studies' results were based on self-administered surveys of Air Force RPA personnel, including pilots, from squadrons in Air Combat Command, Air Force Special Operations Command, the Air National Guard, and the Air Force Reserve. The surveys were administered in 2011 and 2012 with response rates from RPA squadrons that ranged from 24 to 98 percent. The surveys included questions related to exhaustion, distress, and post-traumatic stress disorder.

We also interviewed the researchers who conducted these studies to clarify our understanding of their methods, findings, and recommendations to alleviate the stress of RPA personnel. In addition, we analyzed a report prepared for the Air Force Medical Support Agency that describes the defining characteristics of being deployed-on-station and examines the challenges that personnel who are deployed-on-station face.[43] To obtain a firsthand account of the challenging working conditions that RPA pilots face, we conducted focus groups with pilots at Beale, Cannon, and Creech Air Force Bases. We also interviewed leadership officials at these bases to obtain their perspective on the challenges that RPA pilots in their units face. Moreover, we interviewed mental-health professionals at each of the bases we visited to obtain their perspectives on the working conditions of RPA pilots and any effects on their quality of life.

To evaluate actions the Air Force has taken to address the challenging working conditions RPA pilots face, we analyzed the recommendations that were included in the studies conducted by the Air Force School of Aerospace Medicine and the report prepared for the Air Force Medical Support Agency. We also obtained and analyzed documentation provided by the Air Force Medical Support Agency that describes actions the Air Force has taken in response to these recommendations and we interviewed officials from this agency to further understand these actions. Furthermore, we interviewed and obtained information from officials in the Air Force Office of Manpower, Personnel and Services Policy and the Office of Operations, Plans and Requirements Policy to determine any actions the Air Force has taken to alleviate the challenging working conditions that RPA pilots face. We also obtained information from commanders and mental-health professionals at each of the bases we visited to understand actions they have taken to address the challenging working conditions that RPA pilots face and that affect their quality of life.

To evaluate the extent to which the Air Force analyzes the promotion rates of RPA pilots, we applied criteria from common statistical practices, which indicate that when analyzing relationships between selected factors and a given outcome researchers should account for other key factors that could also explain that relationship. To understand the context of Air Force officer promotions, we reviewed relevant laws and Air Force guidance including the Defense Officer Personnel Management Act[44] and Air Force Instruction 36-2501.[45] To identify the promotion rates of Air Force RPA pilots and how their promotion rates compared to officers in other careers in the Air Force, we analyzed promotion-rate data for officers in the Line of the Air Force competitive category who were promoted "in-the-zone" to the ranks of major, lieutenant colonel, and colonel. We analyzed data from 2006 to the most-recently available data, which for promotion to major and colonel was 2012 and for promotion to lieutenant colonel was 2013.

We focused on Line of the Air Force officers, because RPA pilots are included in this category. We focused on officers promoted in-the-zone because this zone is the point in an officer's career when his or her opportunity for promotion is the highest. We focused on rates of promotion to the ranks of major, lieutenant colonel, and colonel because the promotion rates from second lieutenant to first lieutenant and from first lieutenant to captain are nearly 100 percent, and hence the first competitive promotion opportunity for an Air Force officer occurs as he or she becomes eligible for promotion to the rank of major. In addition, we did not evaluate promotion rates above colonel because no RPA pilots have been promoted to the general officer ranks in the Air Force yet.

To identify the percentile of RPA pilot promotion rates compared to other line officer career fields, we analyzed data on the range of promotion rates of active-duty officers from the careers that competed in the promotion zone on each promotion board to the ranks of major, lieutenant colonel, and colonel from 2006 to 2013. For this analysis, the promotion rate of RPA pilots includes the rate for permanent RPA pilots (i.e., RPA pilots and recategorized RPA pilots) as well as temporary RPA pilots (i.e., manned-aircraft pilots serving assignments in RPA squadrons and manned-aircraft pilot training graduates). For this analysis all of the listed career fields are mutually exclusive. That is, if a temporary RPA pilot was identified as an RPA pilot in this analysis, the pilot was not included in the data to calculate promotion rates for other careers such as the manned- aircraft career fields. For each promotion board, officers from between 22 and 33 careers competed for promotion. This analysis excludes career fields where fewer than 10 officers were eligible for promotion, because the rate of promotion in these cases is highly sensitive to the outcomes of single individuals. However, we included the results from 8 boards in which fewer than 10 RPA pilots competed for promotion to provide a more-comprehensive account of RPA pilot promotions. The promotionrate that we calculate for these instances should be considered cautiously since the outcome of one or two individuals could have a large effect on the overall rate. Fewer than 10 RPA pilots were eligible for promotion to the rank of lieutenant colonel for the first 2006 board as well as the 2007 and 2008 boards. In addition, fewer than 10 RPA pilots were eligible for promotion to the rank of colonel for the 2006, 2007, 2008, and both of the 2009 promotion boards. We obtained these data from the Air Force Personnel Center (AFPC), and to understand the methods AFPC used to collect, store, and maintain these data, we interviewed officials from AFPC and reviewed documentation they provided, and we found the data to be reliable for our purposes.

To evaluate steps the Air Force took to analyze the promotion rates of RPA pilots and the reasons that these rates have been lower than average, we interviewed Air Force officials in headquarters personnel offices as well as AFPC offices. In addition, we evaluated documentation of AFPC's analysis of officer promotions rates including the results of AFPC's logistic regression identifying the factors that are related to officer promotion. We also reviewed the August 2013 report[46] that the Air Force provided to Congress on the promotion rates of RPA pilots in which the Air Force identifies reasons for lower promotion rates of RPA pilots. To identify actions the Air Force took to respond to low RPA pilot promotion rates, we evaluated relevant documentation including instructions the Secretary of the Air Force has provided to promotion board members since 2008 in which the Secretary communicates the importance of promoting RPA pilots. We also reviewed briefings that Air Force headquarters offices as well as AFPC prepared for the Secretary of the Air Force on additional steps the Air Force took to address low RPA pilot promotion rates. We also analyzed the Air Force's August 2013 report to Congress and additional documentation that the Air Force provided about its plans to raise promotion rates of RPA pilots.

As we noted earlier, to obtain the perspectives of RPA pilots related to each of our three objectives we conducted 10 focus groups that each consisted of between six and nine active-duty RPA pilots during site visits to Beale, Cannon, and Creech Air Force Bases. To conduct these focus groups we randomly selected RPA pilots to participate, asked them a structured set of questions during meetings that lasted about 90 minutes, and took detailed notes. We then evaluated these notes using content analysis to develop our findings. We discuss the methods we used to select our participants, develop questions, conduct the focus-group meetings, and analyze the information we obtained in the focus groups, and the results of our analysis, in more detail in appendix II.

We conducted this performance audit from February 2013 to April 2014 in accordance with generally accepted government auditing standards. Those standards require that we plan and perform the audit to obtain sufficient, appropriate evidence to provide a reasonable basis for our findings and conclusions based on our audit objectives. We believe that the evidence obtained provides a reasonable basis for our findings and conclusions based on our audit objectives.

APPENDIX II. FOCUS-GROUP METHODOLOGY AND RESULTS

To obtain the perspectives of pilots of remotely piloted aircraft (RPA) related to each of our three objectives, we conducted 10 focus group meetings with active-duty RPA pilots during site visits to Beale, Cannon, and Creech Air Force Bases. We decided to visit the three bases we selected because more RPA pilots are stationed at these bases than other Air Force bases. We specifically included Beale Air Force base because we wanted to obtain the perspectives of the RPA pilots who fly the RQ-4 (Global Hawk) who are stationed there. In addition, we selected Cannon Air Force Base because we wanted to obtain the perspectives of RPA pilots assigned to the Air Force Special Operations Command.

To select specific RPA pilots to participate in our focus groups, we obtained documentation that included lists of the RPA pilots stationed at each base as well as the amount of time each had served flying RPAs, and their ranks. To obtain a variety of perspectives, we randomly selected pilots with various amounts of experience flying RPAs and we included pilots of various ranks in our groups. These groups typically consisted of six to nine participants.

To conduct the focus groups, a GAO moderator followed a protocol that included prompts, instructions to the participants, and a set of three questions, each with several follow-up questions. We pretested this protocol at Beale Air Force base and used it at the remaining two bases. We used the same set of questions from this protocol for each of the 10 focus groups we conducted. These questions are reprinted below. During each focus group, the GAO moderator asked questions related to the topics of our review to participants who, in turn, provided their perspectives on the topics. During the focus-group meetings, three GAO team members took separate sets of detailed notes to document the participants' comments. See table 2 for the complete list of questions and follow-up questions that we asked during our focus groups.

Following our focus-group meetings, we consolidated our separate sets of detailed notes for each focus group to create a compiled final record of the participant comments from each focus group. To do this, a GAO analyst reviewed the set of detailed notes and compiled them in a final record for each focus group. A key rule of this compilation was that if one analyst recorded a comment, but another did not, we included the material in the final record. To ensure that our compiled final record of each focus group was accurate, a second analyst then reviewed at least 25 percent of each of the final records. In instances where an analyst identified some discrepancies between the detailed notes and the final record, the reviewing analyst corrected the discrepancy and reviewed a higher percentage of the notes for that focus group.

Table 1. Questions GAO Moderator Asked Air Force Remotely Piloted Aircraft (RPA) Pilots during Focus Group Meetings at Beale, Cannon, and Creech Air Force Bases

Promotion
1. As an RPA pilot, what has been your perception of your chances of promotion?
a. What factors do you think contribute to different promotions rates of RPA pilots? Has it been possible to attend professional military education in residence?
b. As an RPA pilot, have you experienced challenges pursuing any other career-development activities, like completing an advanced academic degree?
c. For pilots who previously flew manned aircraft, how does your ability to pursue career-development activities compare with the ability to do so as a pilot of the manned aircraft?
d. What effects do perceptions of differences in promotion rates have on squadron morale? Quality of Life
2. How would you say being an RPA pilot has impacted your quality of life?
a. For pilots who previously flew manned aircraft, how does the level of stress as an RPA pilot compare to your level of stress as a pilot of the manned aircraft?
b. What aspects of being an RPA pilot do you think increase or decrease stress levels?
c. What about manning shortages in your squadron?
d. (If YES) What effects do manning shortages have on your level of stress?
e. (If YES) What effects do manning shortages have on squadron morale?
f. If being an RPA pilot has increased or decreased your levels of stress, what has the impact been?
g. As an RPA pilot, are you aware of any options that the leadership has made available to reduce stress?
h. What are the positive and negative aspects of conducting warfare operations away from the kinetic battlefield? Other Personnel Challenges
3. Do you face any other challenges in your work, such as training issues, that we have not addressed today?
a. What about training exercises and the tempo of operations?

Source: GAO.

Next, we used content analysis to analyze the final records of each focus group to identify themes that participants expressed across all or most of the groups. To do this, three GAO analysts first met to discuss and agree on a preliminary set of themes. We then analyzed an initial set of the records and counted instances that we observed these initial themes. We then reconvened as a group to discuss and agree on additional themes to add to our analysis and to consolidate and delete others. We then analyzed our records and made coding decisions. Following the initial analysis by one analyst, a second analyst independently reviewed all of the coding decisions that the first analyst made for each of the records. Where there were discrepancies, the analysts reviewed one another's coding and rationale for their coding decisions and reached a consensus on which codes should be used. See figure 8 for the complete results of our analysis.

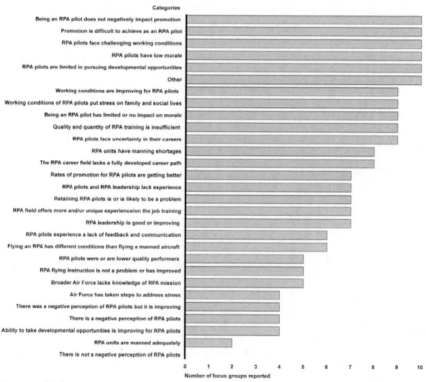

Source: GAO.

Figure 8. Results of GAO Analysis of Focus Groups Meetings of RPA Pilots.

When describing the results of our analysis of our focus groups in this report, we use the term "some," as in "pilots in some focus groups," to report topics that were discussed by RPA pilots in two to four of our focus groups. The information we present from our focus groups accurately captures the opinions provided by the RPA pilots who attended the 10 focus groups at the three Air Force Bases we visited. However these opinions cannot be generalized to all of the RPA pilots at the three Air Force Bases we visited or to all RPA pilots in the Air Force. The results of our analyses of the opinions of RPA pilots we obtained during our focus groups are not generalizable because the Air Force Bases we selected are not necessarily representative of all of the Air Force Bases that contain RPA squadrons and the RPA pilots included in our focus groups are not necessarily representative of all of the RPA pilots in the Air Force.

End Notes

[1] Air Force, *Unmanned Aircraft Systems Flight Plan 2009-2047* (May, 18 2009).
[2] Pace of operations refers to the number of aircraft flying hours and it increases with the intensity and number of operations. In fiscal year 2013, the Air Force flew its Predator and Reaper systems for over 300,000 hours, combined.
[3] See, for example, GAO, *Defense Acquisitions: Greater Synergies Possible for DOD's Intelligence, Surveillance, and Reconnaissance Systems*, GAO-07-578 (Washington, D.C.: May 17, 2007); *Unmanned Aircraft Systems: Advance Coordination and Increased Visibility Needed to Optimize Capabilities*, GAO-07-836 (Washington, D.C.: July 11, 2007); *Unmanned Aircraft Systems: Additional Actions Needed to Improve Management and Integration of DOD Efforts to Support Warfighter Needs*, GAO-09-175 (Washington, D.C.: Nov. 14, 2008); and *Defense Acquisitions: Opportunities Exist to Achieve Greater Commonality and Efficiencies among Unmanned Aircraft Systems*, GAO-09-520 (Washington, D.C.: July 30, 2009).
[4] GAO, *Unmanned Aircraft Systems: Comprehensive Planning and a Results-Oriented Training Strategy Are Needed to Support Growing Inventories*, GAO-10-331 (Washington, D.C.: Mar. 26, 2010).
[5] National Defense Authorization Act for Fiscal Year 2013, Pub. L. No. 112-239, § 527 (2013).
[6] GAO, *A Model of Strategic Human Capital Management*, GAO-02-373SP (Washington, D.C.: Mar. 15, 2002). See also applications of this model in evaluations of DOD personnel management in GAO, *Defense Space Activities: Management Actions Are Needed to Better Identify, Track, and Train Air Force Space Personnel*, GAO-06-908 (Washington, D.C.: Sept. 21, 2006) and *Defense Management: Actions Needed to Ensure National Guard and Reserve Headquarters Are Sized to be Efficient*, GAO-14-71 (Washington D.C.: Nov. 12, 2013).
[7] GAO
[8] We evaluated promotion rates of officers in the Line of the Air Force competitive category, which includes RPA pilots. In addition, we focused our analysis on officers who were promoted in the zone. We discuss competitive categories and officer promotion timing in more detail in the background section of this report.
[9] Air Force, *Report on Education and Training and Promotion Rates for Air Force Pilots of Remotely Piloted Aircraft* (August 2013).
[10] This cost is an average of the $679,552 that the Air Force spends to train fighter or bomber pilots during Undergraduate Pilot Training and the $434,418 that it spends for cargo or tanker pilots during the same training. Air Education and Training Command officials stated that fuel costs were the primary reason for the differences between the cost to train fighter and bomber pilots versus cargo and tanker pilots.

[11] See 10 U.S.C. § 611, et seq.

[12] Additional competitive categories in the Air Force include the judge advocate and chaplain competitive categories as well as several competitive categories for a variety of medical career fields.

[13] Air Force Pamphlet 36-2506, *You and Your Promotions—The Air Force Officer Promotion Program* (Sept. 1, 1997).

[14] The term CAP refers to a near-continuous 24-hour flight presence of an RPA. This includes time en route to and from the target area. Based on the distance to the target, more than one CAP may be required for 24-hour continuous coverage of a geographic point. A CAP requires around four RPAs—three in-theater and one at a U.S. Air Force base for training purposes.

[15] The Air Force conducted the personnel requirements study in response to concerns that the Office of the Secretary of Defense expressed that a preliminary crew ratio the Air Force established in Air Force policy of 10:1 was too high. The Air Force based the preliminary crew ratio on commanders' experiences operating RPA squadrons, and although the study recommended a crew ratio of 9:1, the Air Force decided to retain the 10:1 crew ratio in guidance.

[16] Air Force Instruction 38-201, *Management of Manpower Requirements and Authorizations* (May 14, 2013).

[17] As of December 2013, the Air Force had 175 RPA training-position billets and 111 RPA staff billets across the Air Force major commands, including Air Combat Command, Air Force Special Operations Command, and Headquarters Air Force, among others.

[18] GAO

[19] Air Force Instruction 65-503, *Authorized Aircrew Composition-Active Forces*, table A36-1 (Feb. 1, 2012).

[20] We use the term "some," as in "pilots in some focus groups," to report topics that were discussed by RPA pilots in two to four of our focus groups.

[21] The crew ratio for units that operate the RQ-4 Global Hawk RPA is set at 15:1 in Air Force policy. However, it is not clear that this crew ratio is appropriate because the Air Force's manpower study focused on the personnel requirements for MQ-1 squadrons and did not evaluate RQ-4 squadrons.

[22] Air Force Instruction 65-503, table A36-1 (Feb. 1, 2012).

[23] Air Force, *Unmanned Aircraft Systems Flight Plan 2009-2047* (May 18, 2009).

[24] For example, one RPA unit had to spend about 95 percent of its work hours in fiscal year 2013 flying combat-operations missions and the remaining 5 percent flying training missions, logging around 19,600 hours flying combat missions, compared to about 940 hours of training missions.

[25] Development opportunities can include changes in base assignments or assignments within the squadron, wing, or staff levels, as well as completing professional military education in-residence or via correspondence, which is a primary component of an officer's professional development.

[26] DOD defines operational access as the ability to project military force into an operational area with sufficient freedom of action to accomplish the mission. Antiaccess refers to those actions and capabilities designed to prevent an opposing force from entering an operational area. Area denial refers to those actions and capabilities designed not to keep an opposing force out, but to limit its freedom of action within the operational area.

[27] GAO

[28] House Permanent Select Committee on Intelligence, *Performance Audit of Department of Defense Intelligence, Surveillance, and Reconnaissance* (April 2012).

[29] Often during our focus groups when a participant described a challenging working condition associated with being an RPA pilot, another participant raised a counterpoint to that challenge. For example, during one focus group, one participant described the challenge of working long hours in an RPA squadron, and another participant stated that all squadrons in

the Air Force require pilots to work long hours. One or more participants raised counterpoints to most of the challenging working conditions that RPA pilots described.

[30] RPA pilots fly CAPs 24 hours a day and thus RPA pilots may be needed to fly on day, evening, and night shifts. Whereas civilian workers typically work the same, fixed shift for extended periods, military servicemembers, such as RPA pilots, tend to work on shifts that rotate. RPA pilots fly shifts that rotate from days, to evenings, to nights. Some squadrons rotate their pilots' shifts quickly, such as weekly, and other squadrons rotate shifts slowly, up to several months. Research has shown that shift work negatively affects employee sleep as well as family and social lives, which can adversely influence performance, physical health, and safety. See, for example, J. Barton et al., "The Standard Shiftwork Index: a battery of questionnaires for assessing shiftwork-related problems," Work Stress, vol. 9, no. 1 (1995): 4–30.

[31] Air Force School of Aerospace Medicine, *Psychological Health Screening of Remotely Piloted Aircraft (RPA) Operators and Supporting Units* (April 2011).

[32] For example, see Department of Defense, *Report of the 2nd Quadrennial Quality of Life Review* (January 2009).

[33] Air Force Medical Support Agency, *On Telewarfare and Military Medicine: A White Paper/ State of the Art Report On AFMS Support to the Emerging Paradigm of Employed- in-Place Operations* (September 2011).

[34] Conversely, some pilots in our focus groups did not identify being deployed-on-station as a challenging working condition and some stated that they preferred it.

[35] We compared the average promotion rate of RPA pilots to the average promotion rates of fighter, bomber, and mobility pilots combined.

[36] To identify the percentile of RPA pilot promotion rates compared to other Line of the Air Force officer career fields that competed on the promotion boards in the scope of our review, we analyzed the promotion rates of the active-duty officers from all of the careers from the Line of the Air Force competitive category who competed on each promotion board since 2006. For this analysis, the number of careers that competed on these promotion boards ranged from 22 to 33. We excluded career fields if fewer than 10 officers competed for promotion from a given year, because the rate of promotion in these cases is highly sensitive to the outcomes of single officers. However, we included the results from 8 promotion boards in which fewer than 10 RPA pilots competed for promotion to provide a more-comprehensive account of RPA pilot promotions. The promotion rate that we calculate for instances when fewer than 10 RPA pilots competed for promotion should be considered cautiously since the outcome of one or two officers could have a large effect on the overall rate for RPA pilots for those instances. The boards that included fewer than 10 RPA pilots who competed for promotion are indicated in the notes to figures 5, 6, and 7.

[37] Air Force documentation notes that one indicator of the trend to assign "lower quality pilots" to RPA squadrons is that pilots selected for RPA assignments tended to perform at lower levels on flight-safety evaluations than pilots retained in manned-aircraft squadrons.

[38] Department of Defense, Office of the Under Secretary of Defense for Acquisition, Technology and Logistics, *Department of Defense Report to Congress on Future Unmanned Aircraft Systems Training, Operations, and Sustainability* (April 2012).

[39] Air Force, Air Force Audit Agency, *Unmanned Aerial System Pilot Force Management* (Dec. 17, 2008).

[40] GAO, *Unmanned Aircraft Systems: Comprehensive Planning and a Results-Oriented Training Strategy Are Needed to Support Growing Inventories*, GAO-10-331 (Washington, D.C.: Mar. 26, 2010).

[41] GAO, *A Model of Strategic Human Capital Management*, GAO-02-373SP (Washington, D.C.: Mar. 15, 2002); *Defense Space Activities: Management Actions Are Needed to Better Identify, Track, and Train Air Force Space Personnel*, GAO-06-908 (Washington, D.C.: Sept. 21, 2006); and *Defense Management: Actions Needed to Ensure National Guard and*

Reserve Headquarters Are Sized to be Efficient, GAO-14-71 (Washington D.C.: Nov. 12, 2013).

[42] Air Force School of Aerospace Medicine, *Facets of Occupational Burnout Among U.S. Air Force Active Duty and National Guard/Reserve MQ-1 Predator and MQ-9 Reaper Operators* (June 2011) and *2012 Occupational Health Stress Screenings within USAF RPA Predator/Reaper Units* (Feb. 26, 2013).

[43] Air Force Medical Support Agency, *Telewarfare and Military Medicine: White Paper/State of the Art Report on AFMS Support to the Emerging Paradigm of Employed-in-Place Operations* (Sept. 30, 2011).

[44] See 10 U.S.C. § 611, et seq.

[45] Air Force Instruction 36-2501, *Officer Promotions and Selective Continuation* (Aug. 17, 2009).

[46] Air Force, *Report on Education and Training and Promotion Rates for Air Force Pilots of Remotely Piloted Aircraft* (August 2013).

In: Unmanned Aerial Systems
Editor: Lissa Barlow

ISBN: 978-1-63321-474-3
© 2014 Nova Science Publishers, Inc.

Chapter 2

UNMANNED AIRCRAFT SYSTEMS: COMPREHENSIVE PLANNING AND A RESULTS-ORIENTED TRAINING STRATEGY ARE NEEDED TO SUPPORT GROWING INVENTORIES[*]

United States Government Accountability Office

WHY GAO DID THIS STUDY

The Department of Defense (DOD) requested about $6.1 billion in fiscal year 2010 for new unmanned aircraft systems (UAS) and for expanded capabilities in existing ones. To support ongoing operations, the Air Force and Army have acquired a greater number of larger systems. GAO was asked to determine the extent to which (1) plans were in place to account for the personnel, facilities, and communications infrastructure needed to support Air Force and Army UAS inventories; (2) DOD addressed challenges that affect the ability of the Air Force and the Army to train personnel for UAS operations; and (3) DOD updated its publications that articulate doctrine and tactics, techniques, and procedures to reflect the knowledge gained from using UAS in ongoing operations. Focusing on UAS programs supporting ongoing

---

[*] This is an edited, reformatted and augmented version of the United States Government Accountability Office publication, GAO-10-331, dated March 2010.

operations, GAO reviewed the services' program and funding plans in light of DOD's requirements definition and acquisition policy; interviewed UAS personnel in the United States and in Iraq about training experiences; and reviewed joint, multiservice, and service-specific publications.

WHAT GAO RECOMMENDS

GAO recommends, among other things, that DOD conduct comprehensive planning as part of the decision-making process to field new systems or expand existing capabilities and that DOD develop a results-oriented strategy for addressing training challenges. DOD generally agreed with the recommendations.

WHAT GAO FOUND

DOD continues to increase UAS inventories, but in some cases, the Air Force and the Army lack robust plans that account for the personnel, facilities, and some communications infrastructure to support them. Regarding personnel, the Air Force and the Army have identified limitations in their approaches to provide personnel to meet current and projected UAS force levels, but they have not yet fully developed plans to supply needed personnel. Further, although DOD has recently requested funding and plans to request additional funds, the Air Force and the Army have not completed analyses to specify the number and type of facilities needed to support UAS training and operations. Having identified a vulnerability to the communications infrastructure network used to control UAS missions, the Air Force is taking steps to mitigate the risk posed by a natural or man-made disruption to the network but has not formalized a plan in the near term to provide for the continuity of UAS operations in the event of a disruption. While DOD guidance encourages planning for factors needed to operate and sustain a weapon system program in the long term, several factors have contributed to a lag in planning efforts, such as the rapid fielding of new systems and the expansion of existing ones. In the absence of comprehensive planning, DOD does not have reasonable assurance that Air Force and Army approaches will support current and projected UAS inventories. The lack of comprehensive plans also limits the ability of decision makers to make informed funding choices.

DOD has not developed a results-oriented strategy to resolve challenges that affect the ability of the Air Force and the Army to train personnel for UAS operations. GAO found that the limited amount of DOD-managed airspace adversely affected the amount of training that personnel conducted to prepare for deployments. As UAS are fielded in greater numbers, DOD will require access to more airspace for training; for example, DOD estimated that based on planned UAS inventories in fiscal year 2013, the military services will require more than 1 million flight hours to train UAS personnel within the United States. Further, Air Force UAS personnel and Army ground units have limited opportunities to train together in a joint environment, and they have not maximized the use of available assets during training. Current UAS simulators also have limited capabilities to enhance training. DOD has commenced initiatives to address training challenges, but it has not developed a results-oriented strategy to prioritize and synchronize these efforts. Absent a strategy, DOD will not have a sound basis for prioritizing resources, and it cannot be assured that the initiatives will address limitations in Air Force and Army training approaches.

In many cases, DOD's UAS publications articulating doctrine and tactics, techniques, and procedures did not include updated information needed by manned and unmanned aircraft operators, military planners, and ground units to understand current practices and capabilities. Such information can serve as the foundation for effective joint training programs and can assist military personnel in integrating UAS on the battlefield.

ABBREVIATIONS

DOD	Department of Defense
ERMP	Extended Range Multi-Purpose
UAS	unmanned aircraft systems

March 26, 2010

The Honorable Adam Smith
Chairman

The Honorable Roscoe Bartlett
Ranking Member
Subcommittee on Air and Land Forces
Committee on Armed Services
House of Representatives

Battlefield commanders have experienced a high level of mission success in ongoing operations with capabilities provided by unmanned aircraft systems (UAS). Beyond replacing human beings in aircraft that perform dangerous roles, UAS are highly valuable because they possess characteristics that many manned aircraft do not. For example, they can fly long-duration missions, thereby providing a sustained presence over the battlefield. Because of greater demand for UAS, the Department of Defense (DOD) continues to increase its investment in these programs, requesting approximately $6.1 billion in fiscal year 2010 for new systems and expanded capabilities in existing ones. In 2000, DOD had fewer than 50 unmanned aircraft in its inventory; as of October 2009, this number had grown to more than 6,800. Although each of the military services operates several types of UAS, the Air Force and the Army have acquired a greater number of larger, more capable systems that have been deployed to support ongoing operations.

While DOD has expanded its inventories of UAS to meet warfighter demand, our prior work has found that DOD has faced obstacles in overcoming challenges in the development and acquisition of UAS programs and in the integration of these systems into combat operations.[1] For example, in 2007 we reported that because DOD began the UAS acquisition process too early, the related UAS development plans contained requirements and funding uncertainties. We also reported in 2007 that DOD had been unable to fully optimize the use of its UAS assets in combat operations because it lacked an approach to allocating and tasking them that considered the availability of all assets in determining how best to meet warfighter needs. In 2008, we reported that DOD had not developed a comprehensive and integrated strategic plan with priorities, timelines, and long-term implementation goals to align departmental and military service efforts in order to improve the management and operational use of UAS. More recently, the Congress has expressed interest in DOD's plans regarding UAS, for example, in the steps that DOD has taken to develop qualifications for UAS operators necessary for the routine access of unmanned aircraft to U.S. airspace to conduct training and operations.

Integral to the operation of UAS are numerous support elements—including personnel, facilities, and a communications infrastructure to relay signals to and from the aircraft; programs to train personnel for UAS operations; and publications to guide personnel as they conduct training and operations. Regarding training programs, DOD guidance directs the military services to take actions to support joint and integrated operations training to the maximum extent possible.[2] Thus, training programs ideally require access to the national airspace system (a complex system comprising thousands of people, procedures, facilities, and pieces of equipment) and opportunities for ground combat units and UAS personnel to participate in joint training exercises so that these personnel can practice the interactions they will have with one another on the battlefield. However, DOD's UAS operations are subject to numerous restrictions,[3] which can create competition for the limited available airspace and can constrain DOD's ability to effectively utilize training and operational locations. Further, commitments to ongoing operations can limit the amounts of UAS personnel and equipment that are available to conduct training. Because of airspace access and personnel and equipment availability issues, DOD has used simulators (or virtual training devices) to increase training opportunities. To guide service and joint training programs and to assist individuals and units in integrating military capabilities in joint operations, the military services are responsible for coordinating with each other to develop timely publications. These publications describe doctrine, tactics, techniques, procedures, and concepts of operations and can be used to optimize the integration of UAS during joint operations.

As you requested, we evaluated DOD's ability to support UAS inventories. Specifically, we determined the extent to which (1) plans were in place to account for the personnel, facilities, and communications infrastructure needed to support Air Force and Army UAS inventories; (2) DOD addressed challenges that affect the ability of the Air Force and the Army to train personnel for UAS operations; and (3) DOD updated its existing publications that articulate doctrine and tactics, techniques, and procedures to reflect the knowledge gained from using UAS in ongoing operations.

To determine the extent to which plans were in place to account for the personnel, facilities, and communications infrastructure to support Air Force and Army UAS inventories, we focused primarily on Air Force and Army UAS programs that support ongoing operations. Excluded from this review were programs for small unmanned aircraft. While the military services have acquired more than 6,200 of these aircraft, they generally do not have substantial support requirements. We examined UAS program and funding plans and DOD's policies governing the requirements definition and acquisition processes. We consulted the Office of Management and Budget's *Capital Programming Guide* and our *Cost Estimating and Assessment Guide* for instruction on developing cost estimates and plans to manage capital investments.[4] In determining the extent to which DOD addressed challenges that affect the ability of the Air Force and the Army to train personnel for UAS operations, we visited select military installations and the Army's National Training Center at Fort Irwin, California, and spoke with knowledgeable DOD officials to determine the specific challenges that the Air Force and the Army faced when training service personnel to perform UAS missions in joint operations. Specifically, we spoke with personnel in Air Force and Army UAS units in the United States and in Iraq to identify the training they were able to perform prior to operating UAS in joint operations and the challenges, if any, that prevented them from performing their required training tasks. In identifying Air Force and Army unit personnel to speak with, we selected a nonprobability sample of units that were preparing to deploy for contingency operations or had redeployed from these operations from May 2009 through September 2009. We assessed DOD's efforts to overcome these challenges in light of leading practices derived from principles established under the Government Performance and Results Act of 1993 and key elements of an overarching organizational framework, such as developing results-oriented strategies, as described in our prior work.[5] To determine the extent to which DOD had updated its existing publications that articulate doctrine and tactics, techniques, and procedures to reflect the knowledge gained from using UAS in ongoing operations, we reviewed joint, multiservice, and service-specific UAS doctrine, tactics, techniques, procedures, and concepts of operations. We interviewed DOD and military service officials and analyzed publications to determine how the documents articulate knowledge gained from using UAS in ongoing operations; the degree to which information is provided for UAS stakeholders, such as military planners and ground commanders; and the processes that the services use to update the publications. We conducted this performance audit from October 2008 through March 2010 in accordance with generally accepted government auditing standards. Those standards require that we plan and perform the audit to obtain sufficient, appropriate evidence to provide a reasonable basis for our findings and conclusions based on our audit objectives. We believe that the evidence obtained provides a reasonable basis for our findings and conclusions based on our audit objectives. A more detailed discussion of our scope and methodology is provided in appendix I.

BACKGROUND

DOD defines a UAS as a system whose components include the necessary equipment, networks, and personnel to control an unmanned aircraft— that is, an aircraft that does not carry a human operator and is capable of flight under remote control or autonomous programming. Battlefield commanders have experienced a high level of mission success in ongoing operations with capabilities provided by UAS. Beyond a traditional intelligence, surveillance, and reconnaissance role, UAS have been outfitted with missiles to strike targets, with equipment to designate targets for manned aircraft by laser, and with sensors to locate the positions of improvised explosive devices and fleeing insurgents, among other tasks.

DOD has acquired UAS through formal acquisition programs, and in certain cases, the military services have purchased common UAS components. For example, the Army and the Marine Corps are purchasing the Shadow UAS and the Air Force and the Navy are acquiring a similar unmanned aircraft for the Global Hawk and the Broad Area Maritime Surveillance UAS programs. DOD has also fielded other UAS in order to meet urgent warfighter requests and for technology demonstrations. In 2008, U.S. Joint Forces Command's Joint UAS Center of Excellence established a system to categorize UAS in groups that are based on attributes of vehicle airspeed, weight, and operating altitude. For example, group 1 UAS weigh 20 pounds or less whereas group 5 UAS weigh more than 1,320 pounds. Table 1 provides the military services' inventories of groups 3, 4, and 5 unmanned aircraft as of October 2009.

Several major systems—including the Air Force Predator, Reaper, and Global Hawk; the Army and Marine Corps Shadow; and the Army Extended Range Multi-Purpose (ERMP) UAS—have been deployed and used successfully in combat. Because of the resulting demand for these assets, several of the military services' UAS programs have experienced significant growth. For example, DOD's fiscal year 2010 budget request sought funds to continue to increase the Air Force's Predator and Reaper UAS programs to 50 combat air patrols by fiscal year 2011—an increase of nearly 300 percent since fiscal year 2007.[6] DOD's fiscal year 2007 through fiscal year 2010 budget requests for all of DOD's UAS programs reflect an increase in the amount of funding requested by DOD for UAS investments to support warfighting needs, as shown in table 2.

Table 1. Military Services' Inventories of Selected Unmanned Aircraft

Military service	Group	System	Number of aircraft
Air Force	4	Predator	140
	5	Global Hawk	17
	5	Reaper	35
	Total		**192**
Army	3	Shadow	288
	4	Extended Range Multi-Purpose	4
	4	Fire Scout	32
	4	Hunter	22
	4	Warrior	18
	Total		**364**
Navy	4	Fire Scout	7
	5	Global Hawk Maritime Demonstration	2
	5	Reaper	4
	5	Unmanned Combat Air System	2
	Total		**15**
Marine Corps	3	Shadow	28
	Total		**28**

Source: GAO analysis of DOD data.

Note: The military services have also acquired more than 6,100 group 1 unmanned aircraft, such as the Raven, and more than 100 group 2 unmanned aircraft, such as the Scan Eagle. These systems were excluded from this review because smaller UAS generally do not have substantial support requirements.

Table 2. DOD's Budget Requests for UAS (Fiscal Years 2007 through 2010)

In fiscal year 2009 constant dollars in millions					
	2007	2008	2009	2010	**Total**
Research, development, test and evaluation	$1,778.9	$1,668.3	$2,016.4	$2,519.6	**$7,983.1**
Procurement	2,201.4	2,968.3	3,372.2	3,596.8	**$12,138.7**
Total	**$3,980.3**	**$4,636.6**	**$5,388.6**	**$6,116.4**	**$20,121.8**

Source: GAO analysis of funding requests for UAS included in the President's fiscal year 2009 and fiscal year 2010 budget requests, including funds to support contingency operations.

Note: Numbers may not add to totals due to rounding.

Beyond development and acquisition costs, DOD's UAS programs have additional funding requirements, for example, those costs to operate and sustain the weapon system, to provide personnel, and to construct facilities and other infrastructure. DOD guidance encourages acquisition personnel to consider factors, including personnel, facilities, supporting infrastructure, and policy costs, when fielding new capabilities.[7] However, DOD's and our prior work have found that decision makers have had limited visibility over total weapon system costs because estimates have not reflected a full accounting of life cycle costs. In a November 2009 report, for example, DOD concluded that its acquisition processes pay too little attention to weapon system support costs, even though the department spends more than $132 billion each year to sustain its weapon systems.[8] The report also concluded that the lack of adequate visibility of operating and support costs has been a long-standing barrier to effectively assessing, managing, and validating the benefits or shortcomings of support strategies. In our prior work, we have found that DOD often makes inaccurate funding commitments to weapon system programs based on unrealistic cost estimates.[9] The foundation of an accurate funding commitment should be a realistic cost estimate that allows decision makers to compare the relative value of one program to another and to make adjustments accordingly. We reported that DOD's unrealistic cost estimates were largely the result of a lack of knowledge, failure to adequately account for risk and uncertainty, and overly optimistic assumptions about the time and resources needed to develop weapon systems. By repeatedly relying on unrealistically low cost estimates, DOD has initiated more weapon systems programs than its budget can afford.

We have also conducted an extensive body of work on DOD's efforts to ensure the availability of defense critical infrastructure, which includes space, intelligence, and global communications assets, reporting on DOD's progress in addressing the evolving management framework for the Defense Critical Infrastructure Program, coordination among program stakeholders, implementation of key program elements, the availability of public works infrastructure, and reliability issues in DOD's lists of critical assets, among other issues.[10] For example, we reported in 2008 on the challenges that the Air Force faced in addressing the continuity of operations and physical security at Creech Air Force Base, a location where nearly half of the Air Force's UAS operations were being performed at the time.[11]

While many of DOD's UAS operations currently take place outside of the United States, primarily in Iraq and Afghanistan, the military services require access to the national airspace system to conduct UAS training, among other reasons, and personnel and equipment to support training exercises. However, DOD has experienced several challenges in gaining access to the national airspace system and limitations in the availability of UAS personnel and equipment to support training because of operational commitments. Because DOD's UAS do not meet several federally mandated requirements for routine access to the national airspace system, most types of UAS may not perform routine flight activities, such as taking off and landing outside DOD-managed airspace. For example, UAS do not have personnel or a suitable alternative technology on board the aircraft to detect, sense, and avoid collision with other aircraft. The Federal Aviation Administration approves applications from DOD (and other government agencies) for authority to operate UAS in the national airspace system outside of that restricted for DOD's use on a case-by-case basis.

To provide military personnel with information on UAS, DOD components, which include the military services and other defense organizations, have produced several publications, including joint and service doctrinal publications that describe processes to plan for and integrate UAS into combat operations. In addition, DOD components have produced concepts of operations for UAS, as well as multiservice and platform-specific tactics, techniques, and procedures manuals. These publications are intended to provide planners at operational and tactical levels of command, such as joint task forces and divisions, with an understanding of the processes to incorporate UAS into their intelligence collection plans and into combat operations.

Tactical ground units requesting support from UAS, which can range from small special operations units to large infantry brigades engaged in ground combat operations, may use these documents to understand UAS capabilities and how to best incorporate them into preplanned and dynamic missions. UAS operators use these documents to establish best practices, standard operating procedures for integrating UAS into joint operations, and processes for interacting with other air and ground forces on the battlefield. Periodically, DOD components update these publications to include new knowledge on military practices and capabilities.

Generally, these updates are accomplished through comprehensive service- or departmentwide reviews conducted by subject matter experts.

PLANS ARE NOT IN PLACE TO FULLY ACCOUNT FOR THE PERSONNEL, FACILITIES, AND SOME COMMUNICATIONS INFRASTRUCTURE NEEDED TO SUPPORT AIR FORCE AND ARMY UAS PROGRAMS

DOD has policies that encourage its components to plan for factors, including personnel, facilities, and communications infrastructure, that are needed to support weapon systems programs. Extensive planning for these factors provides decision makers with complete information on total program costs and assurances that weapon system programs can be fully supported in the long term. During our review, however, we identified areas where, despite the growth in UAS inventories, comprehensive plans for personnel, facilities, and some communications infrastructure have not been fully developed to support Air Force and Army UAS programs.

DOD Has Processes to Plan for Personnel, Facilities, and Communications Infrastructure for UAS Programs

DOD guidance recommends that acquisition personnel determine a weapon system program's life cycle costs by conducting planning for the manpower, facilities, and other supporting infrastructure, among other factors, needed to support a weapon system, and fully fund the program and manpower needed in budget requests.[12] Decision makers use this information to determine whether a new program is affordable and the program's projected funding and manpower requirements are achievable. DOD components are expected to conduct continuing reviews of their strategies to sustain weapon systems programs and to identify deficiencies in these strategies, making necessary adjustments to them in order to meet performance requirements.

In addition, the Office of Management and Budget's *Capital Programming Guide* also indicates that part of conducting cost analyses for capital assets, such as weapon systems, is refining cost estimates as programs mature and as requirements change, and incorporating risk analyses in these estimates.[13] We have reported that accurate cost estimates are necessary for government acquisition programs for many reasons, for example, to evaluate resource requirements, to support decisions about funding one program over another, and to develop annual budget requests.[14] Moreover, having a realistic estimate of projected costs makes for effective resource allocations, and it increases the probability of a program's success.

Service Strategies Are Not Fully Developed to Supply the Personnel Needed to Support UAS Programs

The Air Force and the Army train personnel to perform functions for UAS operations, such as operating the aircraft and performing maintenance. Because of the rapid growth of UAS programs, the number of personnel required to perform these functions has substantially increased and the services have taken steps to train additional personnel. However, in service-level UAS vision statements, the Air Force and the Army have identified limitations in their approaches to provide personnel for UAS operations, but they have not yet fully developed strategies that specify the actions and resources required to supply the personnel needed to meet current and projected future UAS force levels.

The Air Force, for example, has identified limitations in the approaches it has used to supply pilots to support the expanded Predator and Reaper UAS programs. Since the beginning of these programs, the Air Force has temporarily reassigned experienced pilots to operate UAS, and more recently, it began assigning pilots to operate UAS immediately after they completed undergraduate pilot training. Air Force officials stated that this initiative is intended to provide an additional 100 pilots per year on a temporary basis to support the expanding UAS programs. While the Air Force has relied on these approaches to meet the near-term increase in demand for UAS pilots, officials told us that it would be difficult to continue these practices in the long term without affecting the readiness of other Air Force weapon systems, since the pilots who are performing UAS operations on temporary assignments are also needed to operate other manned aircraft and perform other duties.

In an attempt to develop a long-term, sustainable career path for UAS pilots, the Air Force implemented a new initiative in 2009 to test the feasibility of establishing a unique training pipeline for UAS pilots. Students selected for this pipeline are chosen from the broader Air Force officer corps and are not graduates of pilot training. At the time of our work, the Air Force was analyzing the operational effectiveness of those personnel who graduated from the initial class of the test training pipeline to determine if this approach could meet the long-term needs of the Air Force. In addition, officials told us that the Air Force would ultimately need to make some changes to this pipeline to capture lessons learned from the initial training classes and to help ensure that graduates were effectively fulfilling UAS mission requirements. For example, officials stated that the initial graduates of the training pipeline have not yet been provided with training on how to take off and land the Predator and that these functions are being performed by more experienced pilots. However, the Air Force had neither fully determined the total training these personnel would require to effectively operate the Predator and Reaper aircraft during UAS missions nor fully determined the costs that would be incurred to provide training for these assignments. Officials estimated that it would take at least 6 months after the second class of personnel graduated from the training pipeline to assess their effectiveness during combat missions and to determine what, if any, additional training these personnel require.

Further, the Air Force has not finalized an approach to supply the personnel needed to perform maintenance functions on the growing UAS inventories and meet servicewide goals to replace contractor maintenance positions with funded military ones. Currently, the Air Force relies on contractors to perform a considerable portion of UAS maintenance because the Air Force does not have military personnel trained and available to perform this function. For example, contractors perform approximately 75 percent of organization-level maintenance requirements for the Air Combat Command's Predator and Reaper UAS. According to the Air Force's UAS *Flight Plan*,[15] replacing contractor maintenance personnel with military personnel would enable the Air Force to develop a robust training pipeline and to build a sustainable career field for UAS maintenance, while potentially reducing maintenance costs. According to officials with whom we spoke, the Air Force's goal is to establish a training pipeline for military maintenance personnel by fiscal year 2012. However, the Air Force has not developed a servicewide plan that identifies the number of personnel to be trained, the specific training required, and the resources necessary to establish a dedicated UAS training pipeline. Officials estimated that it could take until fiscal year 2011 to determine these requirements and to test the feasibility of a new training pipeline.

Our review also found that the Army's personnel authorizations are insufficient to fully support UAS operations. For example, according to officials, the Army has determined on at least three separate occasions since 2006 that Shadow UAS platoons did not have adequate personnel to support the near-term and projected pace of operations. Officials from seven Army Shadow platoons in the United States and in Iraq with whom we spoke told us that approved personnel levels for these platoons did not provide an adequate number of vehicle operators and maintenance soldiers to support continuous UAS operations. Army officials told us that currently approved personnel levels for the Shadow platoons were based on planning factors that assumed that the Shadow would operate 12 hours per day with the ability to extend operations to up to 16 hours for a limited period of time. However, personnel with these platoons told us that UAS in Iraq routinely operated 24 hours per day for extended periods of time. Army officials also told us that organizations, such as combat brigades and divisions, require additional personnel to provide UAS expertise to assist commanders in optimizing the integration of UAS into operations and safely employing these assets.

Despite the shortfalls experienced during ongoing operations, the Army has yet to formally increase personnel authorizations to support UAS operations or approve a servicewide plan to provide additional personnel. Officials told us that on the basis of these and other operational experiences, the Army was in the process of developing initiatives to provide additional personnel to Army organizations to address personnel shortfalls, and included these initiatives in an October 2009 UAS vision statement developed by the Army's UAS Center of Excellence. These initiatives include increasing authorized personnel levels for vehicle operators and maintenance soldiers in Shadow UAS platoons as well as other initiatives to assign UAS warrant officers and Shadow vehicle operators to brigade and division staffs. According to the Army's UAS vision statement, the initiatives to increase UAS personnel to meet current and projected requirements will be completed by 2014. However, at the time of our work, the Army had not developed a detailed action plan that identified the number of additional personnel that would support UAS operations and the steps it planned to take in order to synchronize the funding and manpower necessary to provide these personnel, such as reallocating existing manpower positions within combat brigades to increase the size of Shadow platoons.

Facilities Needed to Support UAS Programs Have Not Been Systematically Defined and Costs Are Uncertain

Although DOD has requested funding to some extent in recent budget requests and expects to request additional funds in future years, the Air Force and the Army have not fully determined the specific number and type of facilities needed to support UAS training and operations. For example:

- The Air Force has neither determined the total number of facilities required to support its rapidly expanding Predator and Reaper programs nor finalized the criteria it will use to renovate existing facilities because decisions regarding the size of UAS squadrons and the locations where these squadrons will be based had not been finalized. In some cases, the Air Force has constructed new facilities to support UAS operations. In other cases, the Air Force determined that it did not need to construct new facilities and is instead renovating existing facilities on UAS operating locations, such as maintenance hangars and buildings to use for unit operations facilities. However, until the Air Force determines where it plans to locate all of its new UAS units and finalizes the criteria that would be used to guide the construction or renovation of facilities, the Air Force will be unable to develop realistic estimates of total UAS facility costs and long-term plans for their construction.

- The Army has begun to field the ERMP UAS and has determined that the Army installations where the system will be stationed require facilities uniquely configured to support training and operations. These facilities include a runway, a maintenance hangar, and a unit operations facility. However, the Army has not fully determined where it will base each of these systems and it has not completed assessments at each location to evaluate existing facilities that could potentially be used to meet the ERMP requirements and to determine the number of new facilities that the Army needs to construct. The lack of detailed facility planning has affected the Army's fielding schedule for the ERMP. Army officials told us that the fielding plan for this system has been adjusted to give priority to locations that do not require significant construction. According to Army officials, initially the Army had developed its fielding plan for the ERMP so that the plan for fielding the system synchronized with the estimated deployment dates for units supporting ongoing contingency operations.

- The Army has not definitively determined, for the Shadow UAS, the type and number of facilities needed to support training and aircraft storage. In 2008, the Army established a policy that directed its ground units to store Shadow aircraft in facilities with other ground unit tactical equipment and not in facilities uniquely configured for these aircraft.[16] Ground units typically store equipment in facilities, such as motor pools, that are not always near training ranges.

Previously, the Army had allowed some units to construct unique facilities for the Shadow nearby installation ranges to facilitate their ability to conduct training. Army officials told us that storing equipment within the motor pool creates constraints to training when ranges are not in proximity. In these situations, units are required to transport the Shadow and its associated equipment from the motor pool to the training range, assemble and disassemble the aircraft, and transport the equipment back to the motor pool. Officials we spoke with at one Shadow platoon estimated that these steps required more than 3 hours to complete, thereby limiting the amount of flight training that can be performed during one day. This practice may also lead to a more rapid degradation of aircraft components. Officials told us that the frequent assembling and disassembling of aircraft increases the wear and tear on components, which could increase maintenance costs. While the Army maintains a process for installations to request a waiver from the policy that would allow for the construction of unique aircraft facilities, officials told us that the Army is reevaluating whether the Shadow requires unique facilities. Any decision to change the policy on Shadow facilities would ultimately increase total program costs.

Because systematic analyses of facility needs for UAS programs have not been conducted, the total costs to provide facilities for Air Force and Army UAS programs are uncertain and have not been fully accounted for in program cost estimates that are used by decision makers to evaluate the affordability of these programs. Further, although costs for facilities were not included in these estimates, our analysis of DOD's budget requests for fiscal year 2007 through fiscal year 2010 found that the Air Force and the Army have sought more than $300 million to construct facilities for UAS. Moreover, as these services finalize assessments of the number and type of facilities required for UAS operations and field additional systems, they will likely request additional funds for facilities. For example, Army officials told us that cost estimates for ERMP facilities would be unavailable until all of the ongoing requirements assessments were complete; however, our analysis of the Army's facility plans for the ERMP estimates that the Army could request more than $600 million to construct facilities for this program alone.[17]

The Air Force Does Not Have a Plan in Place to Address Near-Term Risks to Communications Infrastructure

In general, the military services operate UAS using two different operational concepts. For example, Army and Marine Corps units primarily conduct UAS operations through a line-of-sight operational concept. As depicted in figure 1, UAS are launched, operated, and landed in this concept nearby the ground units that they support and are controlled by a ground station that is also nearby.

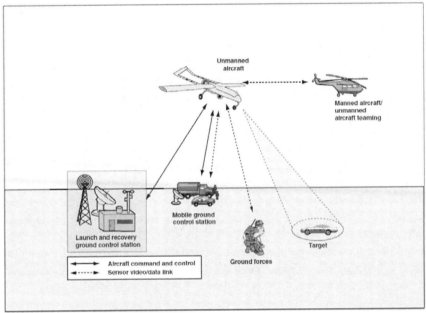

Sources: GAO analysis of DOD data; Art Explosion (Images).

Figure 1. Line-of-Sight UAS Operational Concept.

In this concept, UAS can also transmit video and data to ground units or other aircraft within line of sight to support a range of missions, such as reconnaissance, surveillance, and target acquisition. Some level of risk is introduced in a line-of-sight operational concept if the command and control links to the aircraft are not secure.

Air Force and Navy units use this line-of-sight concept but also use a beyond-the-line-of-sight operational concept that increases the risk of a disruption in operations. In this concept, the operation of the UAS relies on additional equipment and networks, some of which are located outside of the country where the UAS operations occur. According to Air Force officials, the use of a beyond-the-line-of-sight concept permits the service to conduct UAS operations with limited numbers of personnel and equipment deployed within an operational theater. As in the line-of-sight concept, the UAS are launched and landed by deployed ground control stations; however, the UAS are controlled during missions by a pilot and sensor operator located at a fixed ground control station located at a remote site. A satellite relay site delivers the signals between the UAS and the ground control station at the remote site (see figure 2).

The Air Force currently employs this operational concept for Predator, Reaper, and Global Hawk UAS missions that support contingency operations in Iraq and Afghanistan. For these missions, a ground control station located within the United States takes control of the aircraft. A satellite relay site at a fixed location (located outside of the continental United States) relays signals from the ground control station to the UAS so that they can communicate.[18] Any disruptions at the satellite relay site caused, for example, by a natural or man-made disaster could affect the number of UAS operated under this concept.

DOD assesses risks and vulnerabilities to its critical assets and installations using the Defense Critical Infrastructure Program and other mission assurance programs and efforts, including those related to force protection, antiterrorism, continuity of operations, and installation preparedness.[19] For example, Air Force doctrine dated June 2007 calls for the establishment of backup or redundant command and control systems for high-value systems so that operations can continue in the event of failure or damage of the primary system.[20] This doctrine further states that planning for redundant command and control systems should be formalized and exercised before military operations begin. However, the Air Force has not established an alternate, redundant satellite relay site with the capacity to control all UAS missions that are supporting ongoing combat operations. Because of the satellite relay's critical importance in supporting ongoing contingency operations, the Air Force is taking steps to establish a redundant satellite relay site to support UAS missions in the event of disruptions at the current location. For example, officials told us that the Air Force is acquiring new communications equipment with increased capacity for the current site, which will allow equipment currently in use to be available for other locations. In addition, the Air Force is seeking funds to conduct surveys to identify potential locations to establish a redundant satellite relay site. However, officials stated that these efforts are not scheduled to be completed until fiscal year 2012, at the earliest. Air Force officials also told us that they would have options to pursue in the event of a near-term disruption at the satellite relay site, such as relocating assets from other Air Force operations. At the time of our work, however, the Air Force had not conducted a detailed analysis of these options to determine the extent to which they would provide for the continuity of UAS operations, or established a specific milestone to formalize a plan that could be implemented quickly in the event of a disruption.

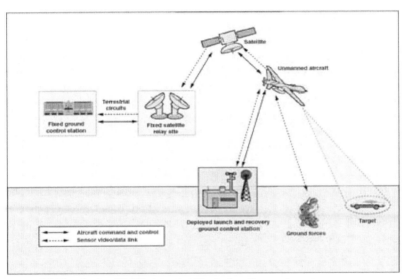

Sources: GAO analysis of DOD data; Art Explosion (Images).

Figure 2. Beyond-the-Line-of-Sight UAS Operational Concept.

Various Factors Have Contributed to a Lag in Planning for Personnel, Facilities, and Communications Infrastructure for UAS Programs

Several factors have contributed to a lag in Air Force and Army planning for the personnel, facilities, and some communications infrastructure that are integral to the operation of UAS. For example, although DOD's primary requirements definition process—termed the Joint Capabilities Integration and Development System—encourages acquisition personnel to develop cost estimates for its new weapon systems programs, including consideration of various support factors, the Air Force's current UAS programs were, for the most part, initially developed and fielded as technology demonstrations. According to the Air Force, these programs have been subsequently approved within the Joint Capabilities Integration and Development System, but comprehensive life cycle plans that fully account for the personnel, facilities, and communications infrastructure to effectively manage the systems have not yet been completed.

Further, to meet near-term warfighter demands for these capabilities, several UAS programs have been expanded beyond planned force structure levels and, in some cases, have been fielded more rapidly than originally planned. Given the changes in program requirements in the near term, the Air Force and the Army have, for example, in the case of the Air Force Predator and the Army Shadow programs, taken measures to support UAS inventories. However, these measures have been taken without the benefit of rigorous planning for the specific numbers and types of personnel and facilities and some communications infrastructure that are needed to support these programs in the long term. Finally, while DOD components are expected to identify deficiencies in their strategies to support weapon systems programs and to make necessary adjustments to them as requirements change, the Air Force and the Army have not completed the analyses or developed plans to account for new personnel and facility requirements, and the Air Force has not developed a plan to ensure the communications infrastructure needed to support its UAS programs. In the absence of detailed action plans that fully account for these factors and include milestones for tracking progress and synchronize funding and personnel, DOD cannot have a reasonable assurance that these services' approaches will fully support current and projected increases in UAS inventories. In addition, the lack of comprehensive plans limits the visibility of decision makers to evaluate the total resources required to support UAS inventories and to make informed choices about funding one program over another.

DOD HAS NOT RESOLVED CHALLENGES THAT AFFECT THE ABILITY OF THE AIR FORCE AND THE ARMY TO TRAIN PERSONNEL FOR UAS OPERATIONS

Prior work shows that in order to improve the management of federal activities, it is important that agencies develop comprehensive strategies to address challenges that threaten their ability to meet long-term goals. We identified several initiatives that DOD has commenced to address UAS training challenges, but DOD lacks a results-oriented strategy to ensure that compatible goals and outcomes are achieved among these initiatives.

Availability of Airspace Limits Training Opportunities

Many of DOD's UAS operations take place outside of U.S. airspace, but DOD requires access to the national airspace system for training, to conduct operations such as homeland defense, and for the transit of unmanned aircraft to overseas deployment locations—requirements that have created airspace access challenges. For example, according to Army officials, a single Shadow UAS platoon requires more than 3,000 flight hours per year to fully train all aircraft operators. Because UAS do not meet various federally mandated requirements and therefore do not have routine access to the national airspace system, personnel must train in DOD-managed airspace and training ranges located near their home stations. Competing for this finite airspace are other units located at home stations that also require access to DOD-managed airspace for their operations, such as manned aircraft training. This competition, among other factors, has affected the amount of training UAS personnel can conduct and their ability to prepare for deployments. Army officials with four of the seven Shadow platoons we met with told us that they were unable to fully train the number of personnel needed to perform continuous combat missions before they deployed for overseas operations. As a result, UAS personnel had to conduct additional training tasks upon arrival in Iraq and Afghanistan.

Plans to further increase UAS inventories on selected military installations will likely further increase the demand for airspace. For example, the Army plans to increase the number of Shadow UAS from about 70 systems fielded at the time of our review to a goal of more than 100 systems by fiscal year 2015. According to current plans, all active and reserve component combat brigades, Army Special Forces units, fires brigades, and battlefield surveillance brigades will be provided with Shadow systems. In some cases, relocations of UAS to different installations have resulted in increased UAS inventories at the new installations. For example, in 2009, the Army moved the 4th Infantry Division and two combat brigades from Fort Hood, Texas, to Fort Carson, Colorado. This move resulted in the addition of two Shadow systems on Fort Carson.

Army officials acknowledged that increases in UAS inventories will further complicate the competition for limited quantities of DOD-managed airspace.

As more advanced UAS are fielded in greater numbers, the military services will require increased access to the national airspace system. For example, the Army has fielded the ERMP UAS to its training battalion at Fort Huachuca, Arizona, and plans to provide one system, comprising 12 aircraft, to each of its active component combat aviation brigades. Because these aircraft are designed to operate at higher altitudes and possess capabilities beyond those on the Shadow UAS, officials told us that personnel who are responsible for operating the ERMP will require access to airspace that they cannot currently access to conduct training. Similarly, the Air Force requires expanded access to the national airspace system to train pilots who operate its UAS, and also to move aircraft, such as the Global Hawk, from bases in the United States to operational theaters around the world. Because UAS do not possess "sense and avoid" technology mandated by federal requirements for safe and efficient operations, the military services must provide, in many cases, an air- or ground-based observer of the aircraft during its flight in the national airspace system. According to DOD and military service officials, this restriction negates many of the most effective advantages of UAS, such as aircraft endurance, and creates an impractical requirement given the numbers of aircraft and personnel that are needed to monitor the unmanned aircraft during training. Moreover, the practice may be an unsustainable solution for meeting the demands of the military services' growing inventories of UAS. DOD estimated in a December 2008 report that based on planned UAS inventories in fiscal year 2013, the services will require more than 1 million flight hours to train UAS personnel within the United States.[21]

In recent years, DOD has taken several actions to integrate UAS into the national airspace system. For example, in November 2004, DOD issued an airspace integration plan for unmanned aviation.[22] The plan established timelines and program milestones to achieve a goal that DOD's UAS would have safe, routine use of the national airspace system by 2010 while maintaining an equivalent level of safety to that of an aircraft with a pilot on board. In 2007, DOD convened a UAS Task Force with the participation of the Federal Aviation Administration and the Department of Homeland Security to find solutions to overcome the restrictions that limit the integration of UAS in the national airspace system, among other tasks. According to an official with the task force, DOD is in the process of revising the airspace integration plan by October 2010 to include near-,mid-, and long-term actions that DOD can take in concert with other federal agencies to improve the integration of UAS in the national airspace system. In our prior work, however, we reported that although some progress has been made to provide increased access to the national airspace system for small UAS, routine access for all types of UAS may not occur for a decade or more.[23]

The Congress has also raised questions about the progress made by DOD and other federal agencies in developing an approach to enable greater access for the department's UAS to the national airspace system. In the National Defense Authorization Act for Fiscal Year 2010, the Congress directed DOD and the Department of Transportation to jointly develop a plan to provide the military services' UAS with expanded national airspace system access. The plan, which is due April 2010, is to include recommendations concerning policies for the use of the national airspace system and operating procedures that should be implemented by both DOD and the Department of Transportation to accommodate UAS assigned to any state or territory of the United States.[24]

Limited Opportunities Exist for Air Force and Army Units to Train Together in a Joint Environment and Available Training Opportunities Have Not Maximized the Use of UAS

Army ground combat units and Air Force UAS units primarily train together at the Army's large training centers and not at home stations. In the United States, the Army has two large training centers—the National Training Center at Fort Irwin, California, and the Joint Readiness Training Center at Fort Polk, Louisiana. Army ground combat units conduct 2-week mission rehearsal exercises at one of these training centers before deploying for ongoing operations. The Air Force, however, has UAS stationed in the United States only near the National Training Center, so Air Force UAS do not support Army training exercises at the Joint Readiness Training Center.[25]

At the National Training Center, several factors limit the time Air Force UAS are available to support ground unit training. First, considerable numbers of Air Force UAS personnel and equipment items are supporting overseas contingency operations and therefore are unavailable to participate in training exercises in a joint environment. Air Force officials with the 432nd Wing, the unit that operates Air Force's Predator and Reaper UAS, told us that all of its unmanned aircraft are deployed to support overseas operations except for those that are supporting the initial training of UAS personnel or the testing of aircraft. These officials stated that in the event that additional aircraft were made available, the wing's personnel levels are insufficient to support additional training events because the unit does not have adequate personnel to support projected operational commitments and greater numbers of training exercises. Second, Army and Air Force officials told us that when Air Force UAS are at the training center, these aircraft are not always available to support ground unit training because a considerable portion of the UAS flight time is dedicated to accomplishing Air Force crewmember training tasks. Officials told us that the Army and Air Force have reached an informal agreement to allot about half of the time that an Air Force UAS is flying at the training center to support Army ground unit training objectives and the other half to accomplish Air Force training tasks. Air Force officials pointed out that although they try to align their crewmember training syllabi with ground unit training objectives at the National Training Center, training new personnel to operate these aircraft is their priority. Third, UAS may not be available during certain hours to support ground unit training, which can occur on a 24-hour schedule. For example, Predator UAS from the California Air National Guard are available to support ground units only during daylight hours. To travel to the training center, these aircraft must pass through segments of national airspace that are not restricted for DOD's use and therefore must rely on a ground-based observer or on chase aircraft to follow them to and from the training center. Because of this reliance on ground or airborne observers, flights to and from the training center must be accomplished during daylight hours.

As a result of the limited number of unmanned assets that are available to support ground unit training at the National Training Center and the Joint Readiness Training Center, Army ground units conducting training exercises have relied on manned aircraft to replicate the capabilities of the Air Force's Predator and Reaper UAS. Officials told us that the use of manned aircraft in this role permits ground units to practice the process to request and integrate the capabilities provided by Air Force UAS in joint operations. However, this practice is not optimal as the manned aircraft do not replicate all of the capabilities of the Predator and Reaper aircraft, such as longer dwell times. At the time of our work, DOD was analyzing the utilization of manned aircraft for this purpose in order to assess whether there is a need for additional UAS to support joint training.

Additionally, when UAS are available to support ground unit training, we found that several factors affect the ability of ground combat units to maximize the use of available assets during training exercises. Officials we spoke with at the National Training Center pointed out that the effective integration of UAS in training exercises, like the integration of other types of joint air assets, depends on the priority that ground units place on developing training objectives that require the participation of joint air assets and their ability to plan for the use of these assets in the exercise. An Army Forces Command official stated that Army combat brigades often focus UAS training objectives during exercises on integrating their Shadow UAS and do not emphasize planning for and employing Air Force UAS. This is consistent with challenges that DOD has found in the integration of other joint air assets with ground unit training at the Army's training centers. A 2009 U.S. Joint Forces Command study found that although the National Training Center provides well-designed training environments to integrate Air Force aviation assets to support combat brigade training, a lack of adequate pre-exercise planning resulted in aircraft that were not fully integrated with ground combat units in training scenarios.[26] The study recommended that to improve the integration of joint air assets into ground training, ground units should conduct planning meetings with Air Force organizations early in the training process to identify mutually supporting training objectives and to synchronize air assets to achieve these training objectives.

Air Force and Army UAS Simulators Have Limited Capabilities to Enhance Training, and Long-Term Plans Are Unclear

DOD officials have indicated that UAS simulators can play an essential role in providing training opportunities for UAS personnel. Specifically, simulators may allow personnel to repetitively practice tactics and procedures and to meet training proficiency requirements without the limitations of airspace constraints or range availability. UAS are particularly well-suited for simulation training given that UAS vehicle and sensor operators rely on video feeds to perform operations, and DOD and service officials have indicated that current simulators have been used to complete initial training tasks for UAS vehicle and sensor operators.

DOD's current UAS simulators have limited capabilities, however, to enhance training. For example, a recent study performed for DOD found critical deficiencies in each of the UAS training simulators evaluated.[27] In particular, the study found that the military services lacked simulators that were capable of supporting training that is intended to build proficiency in skills required of UAS vehicle and sensor operators and prepare these personnel to conduct UAS combat missions. During our review, we also found several key deficiencies that limit the ability of Air Force and Army simulators to be used for training—including the inability of some simulators to replicate all UAS procedures and to enable the integration of UAS training with other types of aircraft. For example, Air Force officials told us that the Reaper simulator will initially be fielded without weapons- release capabilities, which would enable UAS personnel to replicate the procedures used to attack targets, and this capability will not be available until fiscal year 2011. Similarly, the Army's Shadow Institutional Mission Simulator is not currently capable of replicating system upgrades that are being fielded directly to ongoing combat operations, such as a laser target designator and communications relay equipment. As a result, Shadow unit personnel expressed concern that they would be unable to train with these capabilities prior to their deployment.

Air Force and Army simulators are also currently incapable of providing virtual, integrated training opportunities between manned and unmanned aircraft because of interoperability and information security concerns. For example, the Air Force's Predator and Reaper simulators are not interoperable with the Air Force's Distributed Mission Operations Network,[28] which creates a virtual training network for Air Force aviation assets. Officials told us that the Predator and Reaper simulators do not meet Air Force information security requirements for the Distributed Mission Operations Network, which precludes these simulators from participating in virtual integrated training exercises. Similarly, the Army's Shadow Institutional Mission Simulator is not fully interoperable with the Army's manned aviation simulator (the Aviation Combined Arms Tactical Trainer) because of differences in the two simulators' software. According to Army officials, the lack of interoperability of the two simulators detracts from the training value that UAS personnel would receive by performing virtual integrated training with other types of Army aviation assets.

Moreover, the Air Force and the Army have not fully developed comprehensive plans that address long-term UAS simulator requirements and associated funding needs. The Air Force, for example, has not finalized plans to address its UAS simulator goals. Some goals established within the Air Force's UAS *Flight Plan*, such as the development of high- fidelity simulators, are expected to be completed in fiscal year 2010. However, we found that other goals are not linked with the Air Force's funding plans. For example, while officials recognize the training benefit of connecting the Predator and Reaper simulators to the Distributed Mission Operations Network, the Air Force has not identified funds within its future funding plans for this initiative. The Army has not fully defined the number and type of simulators that its active component forces require to meet the training needs of personnel who operate the Shadow and ERMP UAS or the resources needed to acquire these systems. Army officials told us that steps to determine simulator needs are ongoing. Specifically, the Army has commissioned the Army Research Institute to complete a simulator requirements study by October 2010 and it has developed an initial UAS simulation strategy. In contrast, the Army National Guard has begun to acquire a simulator to train soldiers who operate the Guard's Shadow UAS based on the results of a study it completed in 2007 to validate its simulator needs.

DOD Lacks a Comprehensive, Results-Oriented Strategy to Resolve UAS Training Challenges

DOD has identified several challenges that affect service and joint UAS training and has commenced several initiatives intended to address them, but DOD has not developed a comprehensive, results-oriented strategy to prioritize and synchronize these initiatives. A leading practice derived from principles established under the Government Performance and Results Act of 1993[29] is that in order to improve the management of federal agencies, it is important that agencies develop comprehensive strategies to address management challenges that threaten their ability to meet long- term goals. We have previously reported that these types of strategies should contain results-oriented goals, performance measures, and expectations with clear linkages to organizational, unit, and individual performance goals to promote accountability and should also be clearly linked to DOD's key resource decisions.[30]

Table 3. DOD Organizations and Initiatives Addressing UAS Training Challenges

Lead DOD organizations	Description of initiative	Purpose
U.S. Joint Forces Command - Joint UAS Center of Excellence	National airspace system capabilities-based assessment	Outline requirements for national airspace system access, associated gaps, and potential solutions

Table 3. (Continued)

Lead DOD organizations	Description of initiative	Purpose
U.S. Joint Forces Command - Joint UAS Center of Excellence	Joint UAS minimum training standards	Implement by October 2011 minimum UAS crewmember training tasks to facilitate national airspace system access
U.S. Joint Forces Command - Joint UAS Center of Excellence	UAS integration at predeployment training centers	Provide near-term actionable measures to improve UAS integration at service and joint training centers
U.S. Joint Forces Command - Joint UAS Center of Excellence	UAS training improvement project	Develop a series of documents that a predeployment training center or a unit can use to plan, execute, and assess UAS training events
Office of the Secretary of Defense – Acquisition, Technology, and Logistics UAS Task Force	Civil airspace integration planning and technology development	Review and assess operational requirements, identify acquisition solutions, and recommend training and policy changes necessary to fully integrate UAS into the national airspace system to support DOD requirements
Office of the Secretary of Defense – Personnel and Readiness	UAS training and airspace access study	Complete steps, including documenting UAS training requirements, establishing standard criteria for UAS basing decisions, and identifying supporting training infrastructure requirements
Office of the Secretary of Defense – Personnel and Readiness and U.S. Joint Forces Command - Joint UAS Center of Excellence	UAS surrogate aircraft	Provide manned aircraft equipped with sensor packages to training centers to replicate Predator and Reaper UAS capabilities
Military services and U.S. Special Operations Command	UAS simulation studies	Analyze UAS crewmember missions and training requirements and recommend training methods and equipment to sustain training

Source: GAO analysis of DOD documents.

To address UAS training challenges, DOD has launched a number of initiatives to identify requirements for UAS access to national airspace, to identify available training airspace at current and proposed UAS operating locations, to improve joint training opportunities for ground units and UAS personnel, and to recommend effective training methods and UAS simulator equipment, and these initiatives are at various stages of implementation. Table 3 provides a summary of select DOD organizations and initiatives that are intended to address UAS training challenges.

At the time of our review, DOD's initiatives to improve UAS training were at varying stages of implementation. For example, the Office of the Secretary of Defense's effort to identify UAS airspace and training range requirements was established in October 2008 by the Under Secretary of Defense for Personnel and Readiness. Officials told us that as of January 2010, the team had completed initial meetings and data collection with military service and combatant command officials. As a result of these initial steps, the team has identified specific actions that DOD should take to improve UAS training and airspace access, which include documenting UAS training requirements, establishing criteria for UAS basing decisions, and identifying supporting training infrastructure needs. Further, the Joint UAS Center of Excellence initiated an effort to analyze UAS integration at predeployment training centers in March 2009, and according to officials, they have collected data on UAS training at the National Training Center at Fort Irwin, California, and the Marine Corps Air Ground Combat Center, Twentynine Palms, California. We have previously reported that the Office of the Secretary of Defense's UAS Task Force, established in October 2007, is addressing civil airspace integration planning and technology development, among other issues.[31]

Although many defense organizations are responsible for implementing initiatives to resolve UAS training challenges and to increase UAS access to the national airspace system, DOD has not developed a comprehensive plan to prioritize and synchronize these initiatives to ensure that compatible goals and outcomes are achieved with milestones to track progress. Officials with the Office of the Secretary of Defense who are identifying the amount of DOD-managed airspace at planned UAS operating locations told us that one of their first efforts was to determine whether DOD had developed a comprehensive strategy for UAS training, but that they found that no such strategy existed. These officials also stated that while they intended to complete efforts to improve UAS training and airspace access within 18 months, they had not established specific milestones to measure progress or identified the resources required to achieve this goal. Absent an integrated, results-oriented plan to address the challenges in a comprehensive manner, DOD will not have a sound basis for prioritizing available resources, and it cannot be assured that the initiatives it has under way will fully address limitations in Air Force and Army training approaches.

DOD HAS NOT FULLY INCORPORATED KNOWLEDGE GAINED FROM ONGOING UAS OPERATIONS IN KEY PUBLICATIONS

Battlefield commanders and units have increased the operational experience with UAS and have used these assets in innovative ways, underscoring the need for complete and updated UAS publications. We identified several factors that create challenges to incorporating new knowledge regarding UAS practices and capabilities into formal publications in a comprehensive and timely way.

UAS Publications Have Not been Fully Updated to Include Information to Assist a Range of Stakeholders

DOD components have produced several UAS publications, including service doctrine; multiservice and service-specific tactics, techniques, and procedures; and a joint concept of operations, which are intended to provide military personnel with information on the use of these systems, to address interoperability gaps, and to facilitate the coordination of joint military operations. These publications serve as the foundation for training programs and provide the fundamentals to assist military planners and operators to integrate military capabilities into joint operations. For UAS operations, such stakeholders include both manned and unmanned aircraft operators, military planners in joint operations, and ground units that request UAS assets. Because military personnel involved in joint operations may request or employ assets that belong to another service, they need comprehensive information on the capabilities and practices for all of DOD's UAS. However, many of DOD's existing UAS publications have been developed through service-specific processes and focus on a single service's practices and UAS, and they contain limited information on the capabilities that the other services' UAS could provide in joint operations. This information would assist military personnel at the operational and tactical levels of command to plan for the optimal use of UAS in joint operations and determine the best fit between available UAS capabilities and mission needs. Furthermore, military personnel who are responsible for the effective integration of UAS with other aviation assets in joint operations, such as air liaison officers and joint aircraft controllers, require knowledge beyond a single service's UAS assets and their tactics, techniques, and procedures. To effectively integrate UAS, these service personnel require information that crosses service boundaries, including capabilities, employment considerations, and service employment procedures for all UAS that participate in joint operations.

An internal DOD review of existing key UAS publications conducted in 2009 also found that most of these documents are technical operator manuals with limited guidance to assist military planners and ground units on the employment of UAS in joint operations. For example, the review suggests that military planners and personnel who request the use of UAS assets require additional guidance that links UAS performance capabilities to specific mission areas so that there is a clear understanding of which UAS offer the optimal desired effects. Additionally, these stakeholders also require comprehensive information on UAS planning factors and the appropriate procedures for UAS operators to assist with mission planning.

DOD Has Processes to Capture Knowledge Gained from Ongoing Operations, but Key UAS Publications Do Not Contain Timely Information

In addition, many key publications do not contain timely information. DOD officials told us that existing publications are due for revision given the rapidly expanding capabilities of UAS and the utilization of these assets in joint operations. As a result, information on UAS practices and capabilities described in these publications is no longer current. For example, DOD's multiservice tactics, techniques, and procedures manual for the tactical employment of UAS was last updated in August 2006. According to officials with whom we spoke, the document does not contain detailed information on UAS operations in new mission areas, such as communication relay, fires, convoy support, and irregular warfare.[32] Although DOD components have established milestones to revise UAS publications, in some cases, these efforts have not been successful. For example, the Air Force has canceled conferences that were scheduled to occur in prior fiscal years that were intended to revise the tactics, techniques, and procedures manuals for the Predator UAS because, according to officials, key personnel were supporting overseas operations and were therefore unavailable to participate in the process. As a result, these publications have not been formally updated since 2006, and Air Force officials acknowledged to us that these manuals do not reflect current tactics and techniques. While past attempts to revise these publications have been unsuccessful, the Air Force has scheduled another conference in 2010 to revise the Predator publications.

Documenting timely information on the use of UAS in ongoing joint operations is important because commanders and units are increasing their operational experience with these new weapon systems. As a result, military personnel have often developed and used new approaches to employ UAS, which may differ or build upon approaches outlined in existing publications. For example, according to officials, the use of UAS in ongoing operations has contributed to the development of new tactics for the employment of UAS in counterinsurgency operations—information that has not previously been included in DOD's publications. Officials told us that although publications have not been formally updated, some units, such as Air Force UAS squadrons, maintain draft publications that describe current tactics, techniques, and procedures that are being used in ongoing operations. However, these officials acknowledged to us that while UAS unit personnel have access to these draft documents, other stakeholders, such as military planners and manned aircraft operators, do not have access to the new information contained in the draft publications.

In the absence of updated publications, DOD components have captured lessons learned and developed ad hoc reference materials that contain updated information on UAS capabilities to use in training exercises and during joint operations. For example, the military services and U.S. Joint Forces Command's Joint UAS Center of Excellence maintain Web sites that post lessons learned from recent UAS operations. In addition, warfighter unit personnel with whom we met provided us with several examples of reference materials that were produced to fill voids in published information on current UAS practices. Although this approach assists with documenting new knowledge during the time between publication updates, the use of lessons learned and reference materials as substitutes for timely publications can create challenges in the long term. Namely, these materials may not be widely distributed within DOD, and the quality of the information they contain has not been validated since these materials have not been formally vetted within the normal publication development and review process.

Personnel Availability and Service Coordination Have Limited Development of Comprehensive and Timely Publications

Several factors create challenges to incorporating new knowledge about UAS practices and capabilities into formal publications in a comprehensive and timely way. Because the military services, in some cases, have rapidly accelerated the deployment of UAS capabilities to support ongoing contingency operations, there has been a corresponding increase in new knowledge on the employment of UAS in joint operations. This creates a challenge in incorporating new knowledge and maintaining current information within UAS publications through the normal publication review process. Military service officials noted that the pace of ongoing operations for UAS subject matter experts has also limited the amount of time that key personnel have been available to revise publications. As one example, Air Force officials told us that the subject matter experts who are normally responsible for documenting new tactics, techniques, and procedures within formal manuals for the service's Predator and Reaper UAS are the same service personnel who operate these UAS in ongoing operations. Because of the rapid expansion of the number of Air Force UAS supporting operations, the Air Force has not had enough personnel with critical knowledge on the use of these assets to participate in efforts to update its formal UAS publications. Officials told us that conferences scheduled in previous years intended to update the Predator UAS publications and to develop initial publications for the Reaper UAS were postponed because key personnel were supporting operations and were therefore unavailable to attend the conferences. In 2008, the Air Force established a new squadron at the Air Force Weapons School to develop tactical experts for the service's UAS. According to officials, personnel within the squadron will play a key role in conferences scheduled in fiscal year 2010 that are intended to revise the tactics, techniques, and procedures manuals for both the Predator and Reaper UAS.

We recognize that the pace of operations has strained the availability of key subject matter experts to document timely information in UAS publications, but the military services have not, in some cases, assigned personnel to positions that are responsible for UAS publication development. For example, in 2006, the Air Force established the 561st Joint Tactics

Squadron on Nellis Air Force Base, comprising multiservice personnel, with the primary mission to provide timely development and update of tactics, techniques, and procedures publications. However, the squadron did not have UAS subject matter experts on staff who would be responsible for finalizing UAS publications and documenting procedures for the integration of UAS in combat operations, such as in the areas of airspace management and fire support coordination. Squadron officials told us that as of August 2009, the Air Force had not filled its UAS expert positions because of personnel shortfalls throughout the UAS community and the Army had not filled its positions despite agreements between Army and Air Force leadership to do so. According to officials, the lack of these experts also limits the squadron's ability to collect and validate emerging UAS tactics and to disseminate these emerging tactics to warfighters who are preparing to deploy for overseas contingency operations.

Additionally, while a DOD directive[33] makes the services responsible for participating with one another to develop publications for those UAS that are common among the services, they have not yet done so. To their credit, the Army and the Air Force completed a concept in June 2009, which presents a common vision for the services to provide theater- capable, multirole UAS to support a joint force commander across the entire spectrum of military operations. The Army and Air Force view this concept as the first step to improving service-centric UAS procedures, and among other tasks, the services intend to update joint doctrine and tactics, techniques, and procedures for multirole UAS capabilities. However, we found that in several instances, the military services worked independently to develop publications for common UAS and did not maximize opportunities to share knowledge and work collaboratively. The lack of collaboration during the development of publications can limit the sharing of lessons learned and best practices that have been established through the use of UAS in operations. For example:

- In 2009, the Air Force developed the first tactics, techniques, and procedures manual for the Global Hawk UAS, but did not collaborate with the Navy on the process to develop this publication. The Navy is using a similar unmanned aircraft for its Broad Area Maritime Surveillance and has begun operating a version of this UAS to support ongoing operations.
- At the time of our work, the Marine Corps was finalizing its tactical manual for the Shadow UAS, which the service began to deploy in fiscal year 2008. However, the Marine Corps had limited

collaboration with the Army in the development of this publication, despite the fact that Army ground units have considerable operational experience employing the Shadow UAS system and have been operating it since 2002.[34]

- We were told that the Air Force did not plan to invite the Army to participate in the process scheduled for 2010 to update the Predator UAS tactics manuals. In 2009, the Army began to deploy an initial version of the ERMP UAS, which is similar in design and performance to the Predator.

The lack of comprehensive and timely publications that are written for a range of stakeholders limits the quality of information that is available to serve as the foundation for effective joint training programs and to assist military planners and operators in integrating UAS on the battlefield.

CONCLUSION

Warfighter demand for UAS has fueled a dramatic growth in DOD's programs and the military services have had success providing assets to military forces supporting ongoing operations. However, the rapid fielding of new systems and the considerable expansion of existing Air Force and Army programs has posed challenges for military planners to fully account for UAS support elements, such as developing comprehensive plans that account for the personnel and facilities needed to operate and sustain UAS programs and ensure the communications infrastructure that is necessary to control UAS operations. While the Air Force and the Army have implemented various actions to address UAS support elements, these actions in many cases have not been guided by a rigorous analysis of the requirements to support UAS programs in the long term or the development of plans that identify milestones for completing actions and synchronize the resources needed for implementation. In the absence of plans that fully account for support elements and related costs, DOD cannot be reasonably assured that Air Force and Army approaches will provide the level of support necessary for current and projected increases in UAS inventories. Moreover, the lack of comprehensive plans limits the ability of decision makers to evaluate the total resources needed to support UAS programs and to make informed future investment decisions. Furthermore, the challenges regarding UAS training may be difficult to resolve unless DOD develops a comprehensive and integrated strategy to prioritize and synchronize the initiatives it has under way to address limitations in Air Force and Army training. Lastly, without assigning personnel or taking steps to coordinate efforts to update and develop UAS publications, information in UAS publications will not be comprehensive and therefore will not include new knowledge on UAS practices and capabilities. This has the potential to limit the quality of information that is available to serve as the foundation for effective joint training programs and to assist military planners and operators in integrating UAS on the battlefield.

RECOMMENDATIONS FOR EXECUTIVE ACTION

We recommend that the Secretary of Defense take the following five actions:

To ensure that UAS inventories are fully supported in the long term, we recommend that the Secretary of Defense direct the Secretary of the Air Force and the Secretary of the Army, in coordination with the Under Secretary of Defense for Acquisition, Technology and Logistics, to conduct comprehensive planning as part of the decision-making process to field new systems or to further expand existing capabilities to account for factors necessary to operate and sustain these programs. At a minimum, this planning should be based on a rigorous analysis of the personnel and facilities needed to operate and sustain UAS and include the development of detailed action plans that identify milestones for tracking progress and synchronize funding and personnel.

To ensure that the Air Force can address the near-term risk of disruption to the communications infrastructure network used to control UAS missions, we recommend that the Secretary of Defense direct the Secretary of the Air Force to establish a milestone for finalizing a near- term plan to provide for the continuity of UAS operations that can be rapidly implemented in the event of a disruption and is based on a detailed analysis of available options.

To ensure that DOD can comprehensively resolve challenges that affect the ability of the Air Force and the Army to train personnel for UAS operations, we recommend that the Secretary of Defense direct the Under Secretary of Defense for Personnel and Readiness, in coordination with the military services and other organizations as appropriate, to develop a results-oriented training strategy that provides detailed information on the steps that DOD will take to

- identify and address the effects of competition and airspace restrictions on UAS training,
- increase the opportunities that Army ground units and Air Force UAS personnel have to train together in a joint environment,
- maximize the use of available assets in training exercises, and
- upgrade UAS simulation capabilities to enhance training.

At a minimum, the strategy should describe overarching goals, the priority and interrelationships among initiatives, progress made to date, milestones for achieving goals, and the resources required to accomplish the strategy's goals.

To help ensure that all stakeholders, including unmanned aircraft operators, military planners, and ground units, have comprehensive and timely information on UAS practices and capabilities, we recommend that the Secretary of Defense direct the Secretary of the Air Force and the Secretary of the Army to assign personnel to update key UAS publications. We also recommend that the Secretary of Defense direct the Secretary of the Air Force, the Secretary of the Army, and the Secretary of the Navy to take steps to coordinate the efforts to develop publications for those UAS where there is commonality among the services.

AGENCY COMMENTS AND OUR EVALUATION

In written comments on a draft of this report, DOD concurred with four recommendations and partially concurred with one recommendation. DOD also provided technical comments, which we incorporated into the report as appropriate.

DOD concurred with our recommendation to direct the Secretary of the Air Force and the Secretary of the Army, in coordination with the Under Secretary of Defense for Acquisition, Technology and Logistics, to conduct comprehensive planning as part of the decision-making process to field new systems or to further expand existing capabilities to account for factors necessary to operate and sustain these programs that at a minimum, is based on a rigorous analysis of the personnel and facilities needed to operate and sustain UAS and include the development of detailed action plans that identify milestones for tracking progress and synchronize funding and personnel. DOD stated that the department conducts ongoing analysis to determine personnel requirements, necessary capabilities for emerging and maturing missions, basing, and training requirements as part of the military services' processes for fielding new systems and expanding existing capabilities and that this planning is based on internal studies as well as rigorous computer modeling, which provides detailed projections of personnel requirements based on anticipated growth and training capacity. DOD further stated that these plans take into account factors that are necessary to operate and sustain UAS, which are applied in order to synchronize funding and personnel. DOD also noted that some planning factors are variable over time and are regularly reassessed in order to validate plans or drive necessary changes. As discussed in the report, the Air Force and the Army are conducting analyses of factors, such as personnel and facilities, which are required to operate and sustain current and projected UAS force levels. However, although the services are requesting funds, they have not finalized ongoing analyses or fully developed plans that specify the actions and resources required to supply the personnel and facilities that are needed to support these inventories in the long term. Therefore, we reiterate our recommendation that as DOD makes decisions to further expand UAS inventories, it needs to ensure that the Air Force and the Army conduct extensive planning, to include performing the necessary analyses for these factors, so that decision makers have complete information on total program costs and assurances that weapon system programs can be fully supported.

DOD concurred with our recommendation to direct the Secretary of the Air Force to establish a milestone for finalizing a near-term plan to provide for the continuity of operations that can be rapidly implemented in the event of a disruption to the communications infrastructure network used to control UAS missions that is based on a detailed analysis of available options. DOD stated the Air Force is conducting a site selection process for identifying a second satellite relay location and that until the alternate site has been selected and funding secured, the Air Force has mitigated risk of communication disruption with a plan for acquiring and positioning backup equipment for the existing satellite relay site. We state in the report that at the time of our review, the Air Force had not conducted a detailed analysis of available options, such as repositioning backup equipment, to determine the extent to which they would provide for the continuity of UAS operations and it had not established a specific milestone to formalize a plan that could be implemented quickly in the event of a disruption. We are encouraged by DOD's statement that the Air Force has since developed a continuity plan. Although we did not have the opportunity to review the plan's contents, we would expect that it is based on a detailed analysis of the equipment that is required to provide a redundant communications capability at the existing satellite relay site and that it includes specific milestones for acquiring and positioning new equipment in the near term.

DOD concurred with our recommendation to direct the Under Secretary of Defense for Personnel and Readiness, in coordination with the military services and other organizations as appropriate, to develop a results- oriented training strategy that provides detailed information on the steps that DOD will take to identify and address the effects of competition and airspace restrictions on UAS training; increase the opportunities that Army ground units and Air Force UAS personnel have to train together in a joint environment; maximize the use of available assets in training exercises; and upgrade UAS simulation capabilities to enhance training. This strategy should, at a minimum, describe overarching goals, the priority and interrelationships among initiatives, progress made to date, milestones for achieving goals, and the resources required to accomplish the strategy's goals. DOD stated that the office of the Under Secretary of Defense for Personnel and Readiness has work under way to address this recommendation and that organizations, including the offices of the Under Secretary of Defense for Personnel and Readiness and the Under Secretary of Defense for Acquisition, Technology and Logistics, the Joint UAS Center of Excellence, and the military services, are participating on a team to facilitate identifying UAS training requirements and develop a concept of operations for UAS training. DOD further stated that upon completion of the concept, the department will develop and implement a mission readiness road map and investment strategy.

DOD partially concurred with our recommendation to direct the Secretary of the Air Force and the Secretary of the Army to assign personnel to update key UAS publications. DOD stated that military personnel are updating regulations that govern training, certification, and operational guidance for UAS personnel. DOD also stated that the military services are active participants in the process for updating key joint guidance, such as joint publications and other tactics documents, and that the Office of the Under Secretary of Defense for Acquisition, Technology and Logistics is initiating development of the third edition of the *Unmanned Systems Roadmap* and the Joint UAS Center of Excellence is writing the third version of the *Joint Concept of Operations for Unmanned Aircraft Systems*. DOD further stated that guidance on UAS tactics, techniques, and procedures should be incorporated into joint functional guidance rather than the update of documents that are dedicated only to UAS tactics, techniques, and procedures. We state in our report that DOD components, such as the military services and other defense organizations, have produced several publications, including joint and service doctrinal publications, that describe processes to plan for and integrate UAS into combat operations. We also state in the report that DOD components have produced UAS-specific publications, such as multiservice and platform- specific tactics, techniques, and procedures manuals. However, we identified many cases where DOD's UAS publications did not incorporate updated information needed by military personnel to understand current practices and capabilities, and we found that the military services have not, in some instances, assigned personnel to positions that are responsible for UAS publication development. This has the potential to limit the quality of information that is available to serve as the foundation for effective joint training programs and to assist military planners and operators in integrating UAS on the battlefield. Therefore, we continue to believe that our recommendation has merit.

DOD concurred with our recommendation to direct the Secretary of the Air Force, the Secretary of the Army, and the Secretary of the Navy to take steps to coordinate the efforts to develop publications for those UAS where there is commonality among the services. DOD stated that coordination to develop publications where commonality exists between UAS is occurring. For example, DOD stated that the Army and Air Force *Theater-Capable Unmanned Aircraft Enabling Concept* was approved in February 2009. According to DOD, this document outlines how the two services will increase the interoperability of similar systems, and as a result, planning is under way to identify key publications and incorporate joint concepts. As we note in our report, to their credit, the Air Force and Army concept can serve to improve service-centric UAS procedures. However, we found that in other instances, the military services did not maximize opportunities to share knowledge and work collaboratively in the development of UAS publications where there is commonality among the services, which can limit the sharing of lessons learned and best practices that have been established through the use of UAS in operations. Therefore, we reiterate the need for the military services to coordinate the efforts to develop publications for those UAS where there is commonality among the services.

Sharon L. Pickup
Director
Defense Capabilities and Management

APPENDIX I. SCOPE AND METHODOLOGY

To address our objectives, we met with officials from the Office of the Secretary of Defense; the Joint Staff; several unified combatant commands; the Multi-National Forces Iraq; and the Departments of the Air Force, the Army, and the Navy who represent headquarters organizations and tactical units. To determine the extent to which plans were in place to account for the personnel, facilities, and communications infrastructure to support Air Force and Army unmanned aircraft systems (UAS) inventories, we focused primarily on Air Force and Army UAS programs that support ongoing operations. Excluded from this review were programs for small unmanned aircraft. While the military services have acquired more than 6,200 of these aircraft, they generally do not have substantial support requirements. We examined the military services' UAS program and funding plans, Department of Defense (DOD) policies governing the requirements definition and acquisition processes, and data generated by the Joint Capabilities Integration and Development System—the department's principal process for identifying, assessing, and prioritizing joint military capabilities and the process used by acquisition personnel to document a weapon system's life cycle costs (including support costs) to determine whether the associated program is affordable. We analyzed UAS funding requests included in the President's budget requests for fiscal years 2006 through 2010. We compiled data from the Departments of the Air Force, the Army, and the Navy and the DOD-wide procurement, research, development, test and evaluation, military construction, and operation and maintenance budget justification books.[35] We reviewed documents that detail UAS operational concepts and we interviewed officials with the Office of the Secretary of Defense and the military services to determine whether UAS plans account for the services' personnel, facilities, and communication infrastructure needs for these concepts, and to determine any actions taken to update UAS plans to more accurately reflect the costs of further expanding UAS programs. We considered all of the information collected on these planning efforts in light of knowledge gained by the services from operational experiences with the use of UAS in ongoing contingency operations. In examining UAS planning documents, we consulted the Office of Management and Budget's *Capital Programming Guide* and our *Cost Estimating and Assessment Guide* for instruction on developing cost estimates and plans to manage capital investments.[36]

In determining the extent to which DOD addressed challenges that affect the ability of the Air Force and the Army to train personnel for UAS operations, we visited select military installations and the Army's National Training Center at Fort Irwin, California, and spoke with knowledgeable DOD and military service officials to determine the specific challenges that the Air Force and the Army faced when training service personnel to perform UAS missions in joint operations. Specifically, we spoke with Air Force and Army personnel in UAS units in the United States and in Iraq to determine the training that they were able to perform prior to operating UAS in joint operations through live-fly training and through the use of simulators. We discussed the challenges, if any, that prevented them from performing required training tasks. In identifying Air Force and Army unit personnel to speak with, we selected a nonprobability sample of units that were preparing to deploy for contingency operations or had redeployed from these operations from May 2009 through September 2009. We examined documents and spoke with DOD and military service officials to identify initiatives that have begun to address UAS training challenges. We assessed DOD's efforts to overcome these challenges in light of leading practices derived from principles established under the Government Performance and Results Act of 1993, which are intended to assist federal agencies in addressing management challenges that threaten their ability to meet long-term goals, and key elements of an overarching organizational framework, such as developing results-oriented strategies, as described in our prior work.[37]

To determine the extent to which DOD updated its existing publications that articulate doctrine and tactics, techniques, and procedures to reflect the knowledge gained from using UAS in ongoing operations, we examined joint, multiservice, and service-specific UAS doctrine, tactics, techniques, and procedures, and concept of operations publications. We interviewed DOD and military service officials to determine which organizational entities require information on UAS capabilities and practices. We examined the publications to determine the level of information provided to various organizations and personnel that are responsible for planning for and employing UAS in joint operations. We also analyzed the publications to determine the degree to which information is provided to the various organizations and personnel that are responsible for planning for and employing UAS in joint operations. Finally, we interviewed DOD and military service officials about the processes used to develop and update publications; any challenges that affect their ability to update key publications; and how new knowledge regarding UAS operations, such as lessons learned and best practices, is captured. We analyzed these processes to determine the level of coordination among the military services to develop UAS publications and the frequency at which documents have been revised.

We conducted this performance audit from October 2008 through March 2010 in accordance with generally accepted government auditing standards. Those standards require that we plan and perform the audit to obtain sufficient, appropriate evidence to provide a reasonable basis for our findings and conclusions based on our audit objectives. We believe that the evidence obtained provides a reasonable basis for our findings and conclusions based on our audit objectives.

We interviewed officials, and where appropriate obtained documentation, at the following locations:

Office of the Secretary of Defense
- Office of the Under Secretary of Defense for Acquisition, Technology and Logistics
- Office of the Under Secretary of Defense for Intelligence
- Office of the Under Secretary of Defense for Personnel and Readiness
- Office of the Director, Cost Assessment and Program Evaluation

Department of the Air Force
- Office of the Deputy Chief of Staff for Manpower and Personnel
- Office of the Deputy Chief of Staff for Intelligence, Surveillance, and Reconnaissance
- Air Combat Command
  - 432nd Wing
  - 6th Combat Training Squadron
  - 561st Joint Tactics Squadron
- Air Force Central Command
  - 609th Combined Air Operations Center
  - 332nd Expeditionary Operations Group

Department of the Army
- Office of the Deputy Chief of Staff, G3/5/7
- Army Corps of Engineers
- Army National Guard
- Army Forces Command
- Army Installation Management Command
  - Fort Bragg, North Carolina

- Fort Carson, Colorado
- Fort Drum, New York
- Fort Hood, Texas
- Fort Huachuca, Arizona
- Fort Irwin, California
- Fort Lewis, Washington
- Fort Riley, Kansas
- Fort Stewart, Georgia
- Army Materiel Command
  - Program Executive Office-Aviation, Program Manager UAS
- Army Research, Development, and Engineering Command
  - Aviation and Missile Research Development and Engineering Center, Joint Technology Center/Systems Integration Laboratory
- Army Training and Doctrine Command
  - Army Aviation Center of Excellence
- 1st Cavalry Division
  - 4th Brigade Combat Team
- 2nd Infantry Division
  - 3rd Stryker Brigade Combat Team
- 3rd Infantry Division
  - 1st Brigade Combat Team
- 4th Infantry Division
  - 1st Brigade Combat Team
  - 3rd Brigade Combat Team
  - 4th Brigade Combat Team
- 10th Mountain Division
- 10th Army Special Forces Group

Department of the Navy

- Research, Development, and Acquisition
  - Program Executive Office for Unmanned Aviation and Strike Weapons, Persistent Maritime Unmanned Aircraft Systems
- Space and Naval Warfare Systems Command
- Space and Naval Warfare Systems Center Pacific
- Headquarters Marine Corps, Department of Aviation, Weapons Requirements Branch

Other DOD Components

- Multi-National Forces Iraq
  - Multi-National Corps Iraq
- United States Central Command
- United States Joint Forces Command
- United States Special Operations Command

End Notes

[1] See, for example, GAO, *Defense Acquisitions: Greater Synergies Possible for DOD's Intelligence, Surveillance, and Reconnaissance Systems*, GAO-07-578 (Washington, D.C.: May 17, 2007); *Unmanned Aircraft Systems: Advance Coordination and Increased Visibility Needed to Optimize Capabilities*, GAO-07-836 (Washington, D.C.: July 11, 2007); *Unmanned Aircraft Systems: Additional Actions Needed to Improve Management and Integration of DOD Efforts to Support Warfighter Needs*, GAO-09-175 (Washington, D.C.: Nov. 14, 2008); and *Defense Acquisitions: Opportunities Exist to Achieve Greater Commonality and Efficiencies among Unmanned Aircraft Systems*, GAO-09-520 (Washington, D.C.: July 30, 2009).

[2] Department of Defense Directive 1322.18, *Military Training* (Jan. 13, 2009).

[3] UAS training operations are generally restricted to DOD-designated airspace because current systems do not meet several federal requirements. For example, UAS do not have personnel or a suitable alternative technology on board to detect and avoid other aircraft.

[4] See Office of Management and Budget, *Capital Programming Guide: Supplement to Circular A-11, Part 7, Planning, Budgeting, and Acquisition of Capital Assets* (Washington, D.C.: June 2006), and GAO, *GAO Cost Estimating and Assessment Guide: Best Practices for Developing and Managing Capital Program Costs*, GAO-09-3SP (Washington, D.C.: March 2009).

[5] See, for example, GAO, *Highlights of a GAO Roundtable: The Chief Operating Officer Concept: A Potential Strategy to Address Federal Governance Challenges*, GAO-03-192SP (Washington, D.C.: Oct. 4, 2002); *Highlights of a GAO Forum: Mergers and Transformation: Lessons Learned for a Department of Homeland Security and Other Federal Agencies*, GAO-03-293SP (Washington, D.C.: Nov. 14, 2002); *Defense Business Transformation: Achieving Success Requires a Chief Management Officer to Provide Focus and Sustained Leadership*, GAO-07-1072 (Washington, D.C.: Sept. 5, 2007); and GAO-09-175.

[6] DOD's February 2010 *Quadrennial Defense Review Report* states that the Air Force is on track to achieve this goal and that it will continue to increase the number of combat air patrols to 65 by fiscal year 2015.

[7] Chairman of the Joint Chiefs of Staff, *Manual for the Operation of the Joint Capabilities Integration and Development System* (July 31, 2009), cited in Chairman of the Joint Chiefs of Staff Instruction 3170.01G, *Joint Capabilities Integration and Development System* (Mar. 1, 2009), https://acc.dau.mi/pm (accessed Feb. 1, 2010).

[8] Department of Defense, *Weapon System Acquisition Reform Product Support Assessment* (November 2009).

[9] GAO, *Defense Acquisitions: A Knowledge-Based Funding Approach Could Improve Major Weapon System Program Outcomes*, GAO-08-619 (Washington, D.C.: July 2, 2008).

[10] See, for example, GAO, *Defense Critical Infrastructure: DOD's Evolving Assurance Program Has Made Progress but Leaves Critical Space, Intelligence, and Global Communications*

Assets at Risk, GAO-08-828NI (Washington, D.C.: Aug. 22, 2008), and *Defense Critical Infrastructure: Actions Needed to Improve the Identification and Management of Electrical Power Risks and Vulnerabilities to DOD Critical Assets*, GAO-10-147 (Washington, D.C.: Oct. 23, 2009).

[11] GAO, *Defense Critical Infrastructure: Additional Air Force Actions Needed at Creech Air Force Base to Ensure Protection and Continuity of UAS Operations*, GAO-08-469RNI (Washington, D.C.: Apr. 23, 2008).

[12] See Department of Defense Instruction 5000.02, *Operation of the Defense Acquisition System* (Dec. 8, 2008), and Department of Defense, *Defense Acquisition Guidebook* (Washington, D.C.: Dec. 17, 2009), https://dag.dau.mil (accessed Jan. 5, 2010).

[13] Office of Management and Budget, *Capital Programming Guide*.

[14] GAO-09-3SP.

[15] Department of Defense, *United States Air Force Unmanned Aircraft Systems Flight Plan 2009-2047* (May 2009).

[16] In contrast, the Marine Corps, which also operates the Shadow UAS, has determined that the system has a facility requirement. The Marine Corps has requested military construction funds to build new facilities to support its systems.

[17] This estimate is based on our analysis of the notional facility requirement for an ERMP UAS to include a maintenance hangar, a company operations facility, and a landing surface for fielding the system to 10 combat aviation brigades.

[18] In addition, the Navy's Global Hawk Maritime Demonstration unmanned aircraft are controlled through the same location.

[19] As discussed earlier in this report, our prior work has identified a number of challenges that DOD faces with the evolving management framework of the Defense Critical Infrastructure Program. See, for example, GAO-08-828NI and GAO-10-147.

[20] Department of Defense, *Air Force Doctrine Document: Command and Control 2-8* (June 2007).

[21] According to a DOD official, in February 2010 U.S. Joint Forces Command plans to publish revised estimates of annual flight hours required for UAS training. DOD's preliminary analysis of these estimates indicates a decrease in the number of flight hours needed to accomplish annual UAS training requirements.

[22] Department of Defense, *Airspace Integration Plan for Unmanned Aviation* (November 2004).

[23] GAO, *Unmanned Aircraft Systems: Federal Actions Needed to Ensure Safety and Expand Their Potential Uses within the National Airspace System*, GAO-08-511 (Washington, D.C.: May 15, 2008).

[24] Pub. L. No. 111-84, § 935 (2009).

[25] Officials pointed out that because of the beyond-the-line-of-sight operational concept, Air Force UAS stationed at current bases are capable of supporting training at the Joint Readiness Training Center; however, challenges associated with gaining access to the airspace needed to transit to Fort Polk make it impractical to participate in exercises at the training center.

[26] Department of Defense, *Brigade Combat Team Air-Ground Integration Final Report* (February 2009).

[27] CHI Systems Inc., *UAS Training Simulator Evaluation,* a special report prepared at the request of the United States Special Operations Command, August 2009.

[28] The Air Force's Distributed Mission Operations Network provides a persistent and secure connection for combat Air Force simulators to perform virtual training exercises.

[29] Pub. L. No. 103-62 (1993).

[30] See, for example, GAO-03-192SP, GAO-03-293SP, GAO-07-1072, and GAO-09-175.

[31] GAO-09-175.

[32] According to officials, DOD's *Multi-Service Tactics, Techniques, and Procedures for the Tactical Employment of Unmanned Aircraft Systems* publication is currently being revised with a planned issuance date in August 2010.

[33] Department of Defense Directive 5100.1, *Functions of the Department of Defense and Its Major Components* (certified current as of Nov. 21, 2003).

[34] For example, we were told that Army representation in this process was provided by a U.S. Joint Forces Command official.

[35] All of the associated costs for UAS programs are not transparent within the budget justification books. We requested supplementary data from the services to provide additional information regarding operation and support costs as well as facility construction or renovation costs.

[36] See Office of Management and Budget, *Capital Programming Guide*, and GAO-09-3SP.

[37] See, for example, GAO-03-192SP, GAO-03-293SP, GAO-07-1072, and GAO-09-175.

In: Unmanned Aerial Systems
Editor: Lissa Barlow

ISBN: 978-1-63321-474-3
© 2014 Nova Science Publishers, Inc.

Chapter 3

FACETS OF OCCUPATIONAL BURNOUT AMONG U.S. AIR FORCE ACTIVE DUTY AND NATIONAL GUARD/RESERVE MQ-1 PREDATOR AND MQ-9 REAPER OPERATORS[*]

*Joseph A. Ouma, Wayne L. Chappelle
and Amber Salinas*

ABSTRACT

The increasing operational demand for MQ-1 Predator and MQ-9 Reaper remotely piloted aircraft (RPA) in support of intelligence, surveillance, and reconnaissance missions as well as precision-strike operations in theaters of conflict has led to a substantial rise in operational hours, shift work, and exposure to combat-related events (e.g., destruction of enemy assets and combatants) for operators. As a result of the continual need to sustain a high operational tempo, there are concerns among line commanders and aeromedical leadership regarding the prevalence of occupational burnout. There is also concern that there are differences across units for risk of occupational burnout and that active duty crew members are at higher risk when compared with

---

[*] This is an edited, reformatted and augmented version of a Final Report (AFRL-SA-WP-TR-2011-0003) issued by the U.S. Air Force School of Aerospace Medicine, June 2011.

National Guard/Reserve operators. This study surveyed 426 officer and enlisted operators (pilots and sensor operators). Although a wide range of stressors may contribute to elevated levels of burnout, the majority of occupational stress was reported to stem from operational stress and not exposure to combat (e.g., live video feed regarding the destruction or death of enemy combatants and ground forces). In general, the results revealed that active duty operators are more than twice as likely to suffer from the facets of occupational burnout involving emotional exhaustion and cynicism. Active duty as well as National Guard/Reserve operators attributed shift work, shift changes, hours worked, and simultaneously serving as a warfighter in theater while returning home and managing domestic roles and responsibilities at home to their burnout levels. Aeromedical recommendations include reducing operational hours, reducing frequency of shift changes, reducing the length of assignments, providing clear guidance and opportunities for competitive career-progression, improving human-machine interfacing within the ground control station, marital and family enrichment opportunities, as well as periodic psychological health assessments to mitigate the risk of burnout among RPA operators.

LIST OF ACRONYMS

ACO	airspace control orders
AOB	air order of battle
ATO	air tasking order
BDA	battle damage assessment
DoD	Department of Defense
GCS	ground control station
ISR	intelligence, surveillance, reconnaissance
MBI-GS	Maslach Burnout Inventory- General Schedule
ROE	rules of engagement
RPA	remotely piloted aircraft
SAR	synthetic aperture radar
SD	standard deviation
SO	sensor operator
SPINS	special instructions
TTPs	tactics, techniques, and procedures
USAF	U.S. Air Force

1.0. EXECUTIVE SUMMARY

The increasing operational demand for MQ-1 Predator and MQ-9 Reaper remotely piloted aircraft (RPA) in support of intelligence, surveillance, and reconnaissance missions as well as precision-strike operations in theaters of conflict has led to a substantial rise in operational hours, shift work, and exposure to combat-related events (e.g., destruction of enemy assets and combatants) for operators. As a result of the continual need to sustain a high operational tempo, there are concerns among line commanders and aeromedical leadership regarding the prevalence of occupational burnout. There is also concern that there are differences across units for risk of occupational burnout and that active duty crew members are at higher risk when compared with National Guard/Reserve operators. This study surveyed 426 officer and enlisted operators (pilots and sensor operators). The survey consisted of items assessing demographics and occupational work-related conditions (e.g., shift work, hours worked per week, geographic location), as well as a nationally standardized instrument assessing facets of occupational burnout that include emotional exhaustion, cynicism, and professional efficacy. The survey was anonymous to maximize self-disclosure from participants and was completed within the operational installation in which participants were assigned. The results of the study revealed that 78 (26.35%) active duty and 18 (13.85%) National Guard/Reserve operators reported experiencing high levels of emotional exhaustion and 48 (16.22%) active duty and 9 (6.92%) National Guard/Reserve members reported experiencing high levels of cynicism. The results of the study also revealed active duty members were more than twice as likely to report high levels of work-related emotional exhaustion and cynicism. However, there were no group differences in professional efficacy. Both groups were consistent and shared positive perception regarding the impact and contributions of their work. Although a wide range of stressors may contribute to elevated levels of burnout, the majority of occupational stress was reported to stem from operational stress and not exposure to combat (e.g., live video feed regarding the destruction or death of enemy combatants and ground forces). For instance, 157 (53.40%) active duty and 65 (52.00%) National Guard/Reserve operators attributed a moderate to large amount of their occupational stress to shift work. In general, the results revealed that active duty operators are more than twice as likely to suffer from the facets of occupational burnout involving emotional exhaustion and cynicism. Active duty as well as National Guard/Reserve operators attributed shift work, shift changes, hours worked, and simultaneously serving as a warfighter in theater while returning home and managing domestic roles and responsibilities at home to their burnout levels. However, active duty operators were more likely to report working longer hours and additional stressors associated with geographical location of assignment, concerns regarding career-progression, and an uncertain future regarding assignment opportunities. Aeromedical recommendations include reducing operational hours, reducing frequency of shift changes, reducing the length of assignments, providing clear guidance and opportunities for competitive career-progression, improving human-machine interfacing within the ground control station, marital and family enrichment opportunities, as well as periodic psychological health assessments to mitigate the risk of burnout among RPA operators.

2.0. INTRODUCTION

The U.S. Air Force (USAF) MQ-1 Predator and MQ-9 Reaper have emerged as dominant intelligence, surveillance, reconnaissance (ISR) and weapon-bearing, precision-strike remotely piloted aircraft (RPA). As a result of their effectiveness, such aircraft are increasingly relied upon in a wide range of military operations worldwide. The increasing demand for such aircraft has created the need for RPA operators (pilots, sensor operators, and mission intelligence coordinators) to sustain multiple, 24-h ("round-the-clock") combat air patrols. This has led to a dramatic increase in operational hours, shift work, and exposure to combat-related events (e.g., destruction of enemy assets and combatants). As a result of the continual need to sustain a high operational tempo, there are concerns among aeromedical leadership regarding the prevalence of occupational burnout among Predator/Reaper operators. Although RPA aircraft may shield operators from the traditional threats to physical safety while in combat, the high operational tempo and unique stressors of the RPA environment may elevate the risk for occupational burnout.

The level of risk may not be the same between active duty and National Guard/Reserve operators. Anecdotal evidence based upon discussions with line commanders and flight medicine physicians suggests that occupational burnout is perceived by line commanders to be higher among active duty units. Although all operators must contend with having to simultaneously manage a high operational tempo while juggling their role as warfighters with their domestic duties, there is concern that active duty operators work longer hours, have more frequent shift changes, and struggle with more career-oriented stressors than National Guard/Reserve units. However, there is only a limited amount of objective information regarding the impact of such operations on the psychological well-being of RPA operators in general. Moreover, there are no published studies to date assessing for differences in the facets of occupational burnout between active duty and National Guard/Reserve MQ-1 Predator and MQ-9 Reaper units.

2.1. Purpose

The purpose of this study is to assess for the top sources of occupational stress perceived by active duty and National Guard/Reserve operators and the differences between active duty and National Guard/Reserve operators on facets of occupational burnout regarding the prevalence of emotional exhaustion (e.g, the depletion of emotional energy and reserves), cynicism (e.g, declining sense of enthusiasm and increasing complacency to work), and professional efficacy (i.e., sense of self-competency and effectiveness at work). To fully understand the concern for occupational burnout among such operators, the following sections describe the Predator/ Reaper aircraft; operator (i.e., pilot and sensor operator) duties; and the various operational, combat-related, and career-oriented stressors common to RPA operations.

2.2. Description of MQ-1 Predator and MQ-9 Reaper

The Department of Defense (DoD) defines RPAs as powered, aerial vehicles that do not carry a human operator, use aerodynamic forces to provide lift, fly autonomously and/or piloted remotely, are expendable or recoverable, and can carry a lethal or nonlethal payload. It is important to note that ballistic or semi-ballistic vehicles, cruise missiles, and artillery projectiles are not considered unmanned aerial vehicles [Ref 1]. The Army, Navy, and USAF operate a wide range of RPAs that involve low-, medium-, and high-altitude as well as long- and short-range mission capabilities. Among the many RPAs within the DoD arsenal, the USAF MQ-1 Predator and MQ-9 Reaper have emerged as critical and dominant aerial assets to joint ISR and precision-strike operations in theaters of conflict.

The MQ-1 Predator is a medium-altitude, long-endurance RPA originally developed to meet demands for a quiet, versatile, unmanned reconnaissance aircraft. The aircraft is roughly the length of a Cessna 172 civilian aircraft (27 ft long, 6.9 ft tall) with a wingspan of slightly longer than an F-15E fighter aircraft. Remotely piloted from a ground control station (GCS), the aircraft is equipped with multiple full-motion video cameras for day and night operations as well as variable weather conditions. It is also fitted with an advanced targeting system of electrooptical, infrared, laser designation, and laser illumination capabilities and is configured to carry two laser-guided AGM-114 Hellfire anti-tank missiles [Ref 2]. The MQ-1 Predator travels at high speeds that vary according to weather and wind conditions, loiters over a target for up to 24 h, and has an operational ceiling of 25,000 ft. The roles of this aircraft, from an ISR to a weapon-deploying asset, quickly elevated USAF capabilities for supporting ground forces and attacking enemy combatants.

The strategic role of the MQ-1 Predator in ISR and precision-strike missions fostered demand for a more versatile and lethal "hunter-killer" aircraft with enhanced capabilities for identifying, targeting, and destroying enemy combatants and assets considered time-sensitive targets. The MQ-9 Reaper is a high-altitude, long-endurance airframe that is roughly the size of an F-16 fighter with a length of 40 ft and a height of 16 ft. It flies higher (up to 50,000 ft) and faster and is more heavily armed. The MQ-9 Reaper features the same types of cameras as its predecessor as well as synthetic aperture radar (SAR) that allows observation and targeting of points of interest on the ground when poor weather conditions create visual difficulties. The MQ-9 Reaper weapons payload may be configured with up to eight AGM-114 Hellfire missiles, four 500-lb GBU-12 Paveway II laser-guided bombs, or two GBU-38/B joint direct attack munition bombs, as well as other weapons such as AGM-65 Maverick air-to-surface missiles, AIM-9 Sidewinder air-to-air missiles, and AIM-120 Advanced air-to-air missiles. The versatility in weapons configurations provides flexibility to air combatant commanders and ground units requesting assistance. The aircraft may also be equipped with a variety of sensors and cameras, dependent upon the needs of the mission.

Both the MQ-1 Predator and MQ-9 Reaper represent significant advancements in the areas of aviation, human-machine computer and satellite-based engineering, visual imagery surveillance technology, as well as weapons targeting and configurations. As a result, such aircraft have significantly expanded both the breadth and depth of USAF air power across the globe.

2.3. Operational Demand for the Predator/Reaper Aircraft

As mentioned previously, the MQ-1 Predator and MQ-9 Reaper serve several functions in the collection of still and live imagery and streaming video to support ISR and close air support operations. They provide critical, real-time information to combatant commanders for identifying fixed and moving enemy assets and combatants, tracking and eliminating enemy combatants, locating and destroying weapons caches, directing and protecting ground forces, safeguarding convoys, augmenting manned-strike missions, and surveying post-strike battle damage [Ref 3]. Such aircraft provide significant strategic advantages to battlefield commanders while shielding RPA crew members from traditional threats to safety [Ref 4]. As a result of their strategic advantages, the demand for Predator/Reaper operations has grown substantially [Ref 5]. The increased acquisitions budget and devotion to further development of such RPA aircraft reflect the vision of USAF leadership that RPA operations (such as the Predator and Reaper) will dominate aerial battlefield operations throughout the 21st century [Ref 5-7]. The increasing demand for such RPA operations throughout a wide range of ISR and precision-strike missions has resulted in the need to increase the number of RPA operators across USAF active duty and National Guard/Reserve units and to develop specific enlisted and officer operator career fields specifically devoted to such operations.

2.4. MQ-1 Predator/MQ-9 Reaper Operators

To fully understand the potential for occupational burnout, it is important to understand the role and duties of RPA operators. The Predator/Reaper aviation-related crew is composed of a pilot (i.e., a commissioned officer) and sensor operator (SO) (an enlisted member). These crew members participate in tip-of-the spear ISR and weapon-deployment operations on a daily basis. They sit side-by-side in a GCS working together in a seamless fashion to carry out a wide range of aviation-related tasks.

2.4.1. Pilot Role and Duties

USAF MQ-1 Predator and MQ-9 Reaper pilots perform a wide range of manual and computer-based tasks to actively and passively control and maneuver the aircraft (Nagy JE, Kalita SW, Eaton G, *U.S. Air Force Unmanned Aircraft Systems Performance Analyses, Predator Pilot Front End*

Analysis (FEA Report), SURVIAC-TR-06-203, Feb 2006; available through the Defense Technical Information Center to U.S. Government agencies and their contractors only). As reported by Chappelle et al. [Ref 8], the duties of the predator and reaper pilots include, but are not limited to: (a) performing preflight and in-flight mission planning activities in accordance with unified combatant command and theater rules of engagement (ROE); (b) understanding tactics, techniques, and procedures (TTPs) for friendly and enemy air order of battle (AOB) assets; (c) receiving, interpreting, extracting, and disseminating relevant air tasking orders (ATOs), airspace control orders (ACOs), and special instructions (SPINS) information; (d) ensuring airframe and supporting GCS systems for controlling the aircraft are operating efficiently and effectively; (e) performing checklists and monitoring system controls during aircraft launch/recovery; (f) flying the aircraft en route to airspace of national interest while coordinating with air traffic control, ground forces, and other aircrew; (g) strategically maneuvering the aircraft to gather surveillance and reconnaissance data over targets and areas of interest; (h) maneuvering the aircraft into strategic positions for the deployment of weapons; (i) assisting in air navigation, AOB integration, fire control planning, and determining effective weapons control and delivery tactics to achieve mission objectives; (j) receiving target briefs for weapons delivery and conducting battle damage assessments (BDAs); as well as (k) assembling target information, locating forces, and determining hostile intentions and possible tactics.

An additional challenge related to piloting the aircraft is the demand to attend to and interpret visual and auditory data from several sources to sustain situational and spatial awareness. Specifically, pilots are required to multitask and sustain vigilance to multiple forms of input from the aircraft, other aircrew, and military personnel (e.g., ground forces). These multiple tasks include translating two-dimensional imagery into mental representations while performing numerical calculations for maneuvering the aircraft (see Nagy, Kalita, & Eaton, p. 4). It is important to note, as reported by Chappelle et al. [Ref 8], that despite the automated nature of the MQ-1 Predator and MQ-9 Reaper during certain phases of flight, the pilot must manually maneuver the aircraft for deployment of weapons, BDA, strategic positioning for surveillance and reconnaissance, avoiding bad weather, and controlling the aircraft during equipment or system failures. For effective and efficient operations, the pilot also works closely with the SO, mission intelligence coordinator, and other military personnel on the ground and in the air for identification and discrimination of targets and deployment of weapons. As can be surmised from above, the pilot must draw from an inherent set of cognitive aptitudes and personality traits to successfully master a wide knowledge and skill set. Nagy, Kalita, and Eaton (see citation, p. 4) offer a more in-depth view of the specific job tasks and duties of RPA pilots.

2.4.2. Sensor Operator Role and Duties

In general, RPA SOs employ airborne sensors in manual or computer-assisted modes to actively and/or passively acquire, track, and monitor airborne, maritime, and ground objects, as well as enemy combatants and assets. They conduct operations and procedures in accordance with SPINS, ATOs, and ROE. As reported by Chappelle et al. [Ref 9], specific SO duties include (a) conducting reconnaissance and surveillance of potential targets and areas of interest; (b) detecting, analyzing and discriminating between valid and invalid targets using SAR, electrooptical, low-light, and infrared full-motion video imagery, and other active or passive tracking systems; (c) assisting in air navigation, AOB integration, fire control planning, and determining effective weapons control and delivery tactics to achieve overall mission objectives; (d) receiving target briefs (9-liners) for weapons delivery and conducting immediate first phase BDAs for up-channel coordination and potential re-attack; (e) utilizing laser target marking systems to provide target identification and illumination for onboard weapons delivery and being responsible for terminal weapons guidance; (f) performing preflight and in-flight mission planning activities in accordance with unified combatant command and theater ROE; (g) understanding TTPs for friendly and enemy AOB assets; (h) operating mission planning ancillary equipment to initialize information for download to airborne mission systems; (i) receiving, interpreting, extracting, and disseminating relevant ATO, ACO, and SPINS information; (j) researching and studying target imagery, friendly and enemy orders of battle, and offensive and defensive capabilities from various sources; and, lastly (k) assembling target information, locating forces, and determining hostile intentions and possible tactics.

As can be surmised from above, this enlisted aircrew position requires a person to visually discriminate and synthesize various images and complex data on several electronic screens while maintaining heightened vigilance to numerous sources of visual and auditory information necessary for sustaining situational and spatial awareness. For example, the SO must effectively attend to the electronic video to calibrate instruments and distances of specific ground objects while maintaining vigilance to visual and auditory input from aircrew and command. The SO must also effectively communicate with aircrew to report the identification and discrimination of targets and to assist in the deployment of weapons. The SO must also sustain visual targeting during and following the employment of weapons to ensure accuracy and damage assessment. This task includes visually observing the destruction of fixed and moving objects (such as buildings and cars), as well as the wounding and death of human combatants. Morever, the SO must be attentive to several procedural checklists and processes with advanced computer systems while simultaneously translating two-dimensional information from video screens into four-dimensional mental imagery and spatial analyses. As mentioned above, SOs must carry out their duties in a confined environment with specific ROE, tactics, and techniques. Nagy, Muse, and Eaton (Nagy J, Muse K, Eaton G, *U.S. Air Force Unmanned Aircraft Systems Performance Analyses: Predator Sensor Operator Front End Analysis (FEA) Report*, SURVIAC-TR-10-043, 18 Aug 2006; available through the Defense Technical Information Center to U.S. Government agencies and their contractors only) offer a more in-depth view of the specific job tasks and duties of SOs.

2.5. Aeromedical Concerns Regarding Occupational Burnout

According to USAF aeromedical policy, performing and operating in a high-demand, high-operational, and high-precision aviation-related position requires an optimal level of physical and psychological functioning [Ref 10,11]. Although operators may be perceived to be generally healthy, if they suffer from a physical or psychological condition that has the potential to lead to degradation in the performance of their duties, then they are disqualified from such aviation-related operations. A general reason for holding operators to such high aeromedical standards is due to the perceived risk that subtle decrements in health can have on elevating the risk for an aviation mishap in which the threat to human life, national security, foreign relations, military operations, and loss of a multimillion dollar aircraft is often high. Although occupational burnout is not a categorical psychiatric diagnosis, it stands to reason that such a condition leads to performance degradation and, if untreated, may lead to significant emotional difficulties (e.g., anxiety and depression).

Occupational burnout has been studied in depth and defined by Maslach, Jackson, and Leiter (Ref 12) as containing three aspects: emotional exhaustion (i.e., depletion of emotional energy and reserves due to work-related stress), cynicism (a sense of indifference or a distant attitude toward work, as well as declining sense of enthusiasm for work), and personal efficacy (i.e., a sense of satisfaction with accomplishments and efficacy at work). Occupational burnout is composed of high levels of emotional exhaustion and cynicism, combined with low levels of personal efficacy. Consequently, the negative effects of occupational burnout can be wide ranging, from impaired ability to complete tasks to difficulty relating to people.

As mentioned previously, the sources of occupational burnout can be wide ranging. An important aspect of assessing the facets of burnout is to understand the RPA operator's occupational environment as a whole. This understanding includes considering the variety of operational stressors (e.g., workload, work hours, shift work, career progression) as well as combat-related stressors (e.g., exposure to live imagery of battle damage, destruction of enemy forces, and duty to protect ground forces) that may impact an operator's psychological health. Although occupational stressors may differ across occupational positions (e.g., supervisory vs. nonsupervisory, enlisted vs. officer), an important aspect of this study is to address common sources of stress.

2.5.1. Operational Stressors

Operational stressors are defined as those related to sustaining operations. These operational stressors include issues such as available manpower, equipment, and general resources needed. There are several important operational stressors to consider when assessing the risk of occupational burnout among Predator/Reaper operators. As originally reported by Chappelle et al. [Ref 8], such stressors include, but are not limited to, (a) long hours (e.g., working 51 or more hours a week, working 6 days on, 2 days off); (b) frequent shift work and shift changes (e.g, every 3 wk), making it difficult to maintain domestic life routines [Ref 13]; (c) geographically undesirable locations (e.g., long commute times, limited base and community resources in highly rural settings); (d) restricted or highly limited opportunities to fly manned airframes to maintain flight hours necessary for flight pay or promotion for those who cross-trained from a manned airframe; (e) restricted working environment (i.e., small GCS with limited freedom for mobility); (f) poor ergonomics of seating and poor temperature control of work stations; (g) sustaining vigilance to a high monitoring visual and auditory workload [Ref 14] and multitasking with time limited suspense (see Nagy, Kalita, & Eaton, p. 4; see Nagy, Eaton, & Muse, p. 6). It stands to reason such stressors can lead to both physical and psychological distress when faced on a daily basis. The long hours combined with rotating shift work can reasonably elevate the risk of fatigue [Ref 14], increase difficulty with maintaining a routine domestic life, as well as elevate the potential for a mishap [Ref 15].

2.5.2. Combat Stressors

Combat stressors are defined as those directly involved in the ISR and weapon-deployment missions that involve direct support to combat-related operations. As originally reported by Chappelle et al. [Ref 8], combat-related stressors that may lead to occupational burnout among Predator/Reaper operators include, but are not limited to, (a) precision targeting and destroying enemy combatants and assets in which mistakes may come at a high price (e.g., inadvertently killing friendly ground forces and civilians), (b) exposure to live video feed and images of destruction to ensure combatants have been effectively destroyed or neutralized, (c) making critical decisions regarding the identification of enemy combatants and providing effective force protection to ground troops to reduce casualties of friendly forces and civilian bystanders, and, lastly, (d) the unique demand for RPA operators to simultaneously juggle their warfighter role while having to sustain their domestic roles and responsibilities. Because of the advancements in aviation and computer-based and satellite communication technology, Predator/Reaper operations provide the ability to conduct ISR and precision-strike capabilities from within national borders. However, this capability creates a unique requirement on Predator/Reaper operators to compartmentalize their warfighter role from their domestic role and responsibilities on a daily basis. It stands to reason that engagement in ISR and precision-strike missions critical to theater operations may elevate the risk of occupational burnout among Predator/Reaper operators who must also simultaneously manage their domestic responsibilities.

RPA operators must also contend with a number of career-oriented stressors [Ref 8,16]. First, the Predator/Reaper career field is relatively new in contrast to aviation-related career fields for manned airframes. As a result, aspects regarding competitive career progression and promotion in unmanned aviation remain uncertain. Second, many Predator/Reaper operators within active duty units cross-trained from a manned airframe under the assumption they would be able to return to their original career field following completion of a 3- to 4-yr assignment. Furthermore, many active duty operators were involuntarily assigned to Predator/Reaper units following successful completion of training in manned airframes. Whether the assignment was voluntary or involuntary, returning to their original career field in flying manned aircraft is limited or restricted. The restriction is due, in large part, to the continual surge in Predator/Reaper operations that require experienced operators. This increased demand in Predator/Reaper operations has left many active duty members with the perception they are in a career field and assignment they do not perceive as inherently rewarding. The lack of control over their assignment process and uncertain future are stressors to which many active duty operators must adapt, which may subsequently elevate their risk for occupational stress and burnout.

Based upon conversations with line commanders and flight medicine physicians at multiple USAF RPA installations, it is largely perceived that when the various stressors above are combined on a daily basis, there is a negative effect on psychological health. However, it is unknown whether or not there are differences in the rates of occupational burnout between active duty and National Guard/Reserve operators. Many line commanders and physicians suggest that RPA operators are at higher risk of burnout. This perceived increased risk of burnout occurs because of the operational stressors to which operators are exposed, such as working longer hours, a larger percentage having to work swing and night shifts to sustain "around-the-clock" operations, and undesirable geographical locations. Some commanders and physicians have suggested that uncertain career prospects regarding promotion and the involuntary nature of Reaper/Predator assignments for many active duty operators further increase the risk of burnout. Regardless of one's opinion on the sources of stress (combat vs. operational or a combination), there is a general consensus that active duty Predator/Reaper operators may be at higher risk of experiencing burnout.

3.0. Methods

3.1. Participants

3.1.1. Active Duty Operators

There were 296 active duty participants from 8 RPA operational squadrons, with 145 pilots (48.99%) and 151 (51.01%) SOs in the study. Among the participants, there were 266 males (90.78%) and 27 females (9.22%). There were 178 (29.96%) between the ages of 18-30, 35 (19.86%) between the ages of 41-40, and 56 (8.90%) over the age of 40. The sample was composed of 65 (22.34%) airmen (E1-E3), 66 (22.68%) noncommissioned officers (E4-E5), 17 (5.84%) senior noncommissioned officers (E6-E8), 103 (35.34%) company grade officers (O1-O3), and 40 (13.75%) field grade officers (O4-O6). Four active duty participants did not report their age and rank, and one participant did not report age. A total of 113 (38.70%) reported being single and 179 (61.30%) reported being married. Four participants did not report their marital status. A total of 186 (62.84%) of the participants reported having children living at home, and 110 (37.16%) denied having children living at home.

3.1.2. National Guard/Reserve Operators

There were 130 USAF National Guard and Reserve participants from 4 separate RPA operational squadrons, with 71 pilots (54.62%) and 59 (45.38%) SOs. Among the participants, there were 123 males (94.62%) and 7 females (5.38%); 27 (20.77%) were between the ages of 18-30, 35 (26.92%) between the ages of 41-40, and 66 (51.56%) over the age of 40. There were 10 (5.05%) airmen (E1-E3), 30 (23.44%) noncommissioned officers (E4-E5), 18 (9.09%) senior noncommissioned officers (E6-E8), 13 (6.57%) company grade officers (O1-O3), and 57 (28.79%) field grade officers (O4-O6). Among the participants, two did not report their age and rank. A total of 32 (25.20%) reported being single, and 95 (74.8%) reported being married. Three participants did not report their marital status. A total of 49 (37.69%) reported having children living at home, and 81 (62.31%) denied having children living at home.

The purpose and methodology of the study were reviewed and granted exemption from the Wright-Patterson Air Force Base Institutional Review Board and assigned protocol number F-WR-2009-0063-E. The voluntary and fully informed consent of participants was obtained.

3.2. Measures

Participants were given a questionnaire composed of items that asked about rank range, gender, age range, marital status, length of time serving as a Predator/Reaper operator, average number of hours worked in a typical week, current work shift, and sources of occupational stress. The demographics questionnaire was developed to allow participants to remain anonymous to increase self-disclosure in a community in which there is strong cultural stigma regarding physical and emotional difficulties.

The Maslach Burnout Inventory-General Schedule (MBI-GS) is a leading measure of occupational burnout. The measurement is a 16-item self-report questionnaire assessing occupational burnout [Ref 12]. Aspects of occupational burnout measured by the questionnaire include emotional exhaustion, cynicism, and professional efficacy. The emotional exhaustion and cynicism subscales are each composed of five items, and the professional efficacy subscale is composed of six items. The subscale of emotional exhaustion is a subjective measure regarding the depletion of emotional energy and reserves due to work-related stress. High scores on emotional exhaustion are likely signs of distress in response to emotionally demanding work. The subscale of cynicism is a subjective measure regarding the sense of indifference or a distant attitude toward work (e.g., a declining sense of enthusiasm for work). The items refer to work itself and not to personal relationships at work. High levels of cynicism may reflect an attempt by respondents to distance themselves from their work as a way of coping with exhausting demands. The subscale of professional efficacy assesses satisfaction with past and present accomplishments in one's occupation, as well as expectations of continued effectiveness at work. Construct validity of the MBI-GS has been established via principal component analyses with other constructs for each of the scales. Stability coefficients range from .65 to .67 [Ref 12].

3.3. Procedure

The participation from volunteers was requested by line leadership (group, squadron, and flight commanders from active duty and National Guard/Reserve units) via e-mail and in-person group meetings. Line leadership stated participation was voluntary and responses to the questionnaire would remain anonymous to support honest disclosure. Line leadership encouraged participation to understand the main sources of stress and levels of stress of those within their chain-of-command so they would be better equipped to initiate changes that would lead to improvements in health and morale. The demographics questionnaire and MBI-GS were handed out to participants in group settings at the work site of each participant by USAF flight medicine physicians, psychologists, or mental health technicians from the medical clinic following a brief description and purpose for participation. In general, it took participants 15 to 20 min to complete all the items on the survey.

4.0. RESULTS

Item responses were summed to obtain total scores for each of the subscale measures. A number of t-tests were conducted to assess for differences between groups. A difference between group mean scores was considered operationally relevant if (a) the difference was statistically significant at the .05 level and (b) the magnitude of the difference was moderate to large as indicated by a Cohen's d effect size of .50. Furthermore, clinical levels of occupational burnout were identified by summing scores on the three scales. Clinical cut-off scores were set at 20 or more on both the emotional exhaustion and cynicism scales and 12 or below on the professional efficacy scale. See Figure 1 for the percentage of operators meeting or exceeding discretionary cut- off scores.

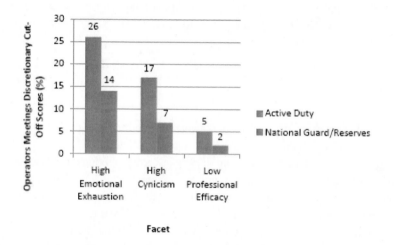

Figure 1. Percentage of Operators within Each Group Who Meet the Discretionary Cut-Off Scores for Each Facet of Occupational Burnout.

4.1. Shift Work, Hours Worked, and Attribution to Occupational Stress

A summary of responses from active duty operators revealed that 149 (52.46%) worked the day shift, 70 (24.65%) worked the mid shift, and 61 (21.28%) worked the night shift. A total of four (1.41%) operators reported working multiple shifts over the past month. A total of 157 (53.40%) attributed a moderate to large amount of their occupational stress to shift work. In regards to number of hours a week operating RPAs, 32 (10.92%) reported 30-40 h a week, 120 (40.96%) reported 41-50 h a week, and 167 (56.99%) reported ≥51 h a week.

A summary of responses from National Guard/Reserve operators revealed 69 (46.83%) worked the day shift, 24 (19.05%) worked the mid shift, and 29 (23.02%) worked the night shift. A total of 14 (11.11%) operators reported working multiple shifts over the past month. A total of 65 (52.00%) attributed a moderate to large amount of their occupational stress to shift work. In regards to number of hours a week operating RPAs, 27 (21.26%) reported 30-40 h a week, 74 (58.27%) reported 41-50 h a week, and 26 (20.47%) reported ≥51 h a week.

4.2. Emotional Exhaustion

The average emotional exhaustion score was 13.58 (standard deviation (SD) = 8.10) for active duty operators and 10.50 (SD=6.63) for National Guard/Reserve operators. A t-test assessing for mean differences between groups based upon unequal variances (Satterthwaite test) was significant, t=-4.16, p<.01. A Cohen's d effect size assessing the magnitude of the difference was .42. Chi-square analyses conducted on the frequency of 78 (26.35%) active duty and 18 (13.85%) National Guard/Reserve operators experiencing high levels of emotional exhaustion (a score of 20 or more on this scale) were significant, x^2=8.09, p<.01. An odds ratio revealed active duty operators are 2.2 times more likely to report high levels of emotional exhaustion when compared with National Guard/Reserve operators.

4.3. Cynicism

The average cynicism score was 10.56 (SD=8.33) for active duty operators and 7.87 (SD=6.26) for National Guard/Reserve operators. A t-test assessing for mean differences between groups based upon unequal variances (Satterthwaite test) was significant, t=-3.72, p<.01. A Cohen's d effect size assessing the magnitude of the difference was .37. Chi-square analyses conducted on the frequency of 48 (16.22%) active duty and 9 (6.92%) National Guard/Reserve members experiencing high levels of cynicism (a score of 20 or more on this scale) were significant, x^2=6.73, p<.01. An odds ratio revealed that active duty operators are 2.62 times more likely to report high levels of cynicism when compared with National Guard/Reserve operators.

4.4. Professional Efficacy

The average professional efficacy score was 26.36 (SD=6.57) for active duty operators and 27.00 (SD=5.73) for National Guard/Reserve operators. A t-test assessing for mean differences between groups based upon unequal variances (Satterthwaite test) was not significant, t=-.98, p>.10. There was no significant difference between groups in mean professional efficacy scores. Chi-square analyses conducted on the frequency of 15 (5.07%) active duty and 3 (2.31%) National Guard/Reserve operators who reported experiencing low levels of professional efficacy (a score of 12 or less on this scale) were not significant. An odds ratio revealed that active duty operators are not more likely to report low levels of professional efficacy when compared with National Guard/Reserve operators.

5.0. DISCUSSION

5.1. Sources of Occupational Stress

The first objective of this study was to assess for the sources of occupational stress and for differences in the sources of stress between active duty and National Guard/Reserve units.

Consistent with the results of the study by Chappelle et al. [Ref 8], the most commonly cited stressors accentuating occupational stress for RPA operators included long hours (50+ h a week), shift work, human-machine interface difficulties (ergonomic design of equipment and GCS), inefficiencies in computer-based input and command procedures, and difficulty juggling the demands of personal and domestic life with military operations. These were commonly cited by both active duty and National Guard/Reserve operators. Important to note is that over half of the participants in this study reported a moderate to large amount of their occupational stress was attributed to shift work. Although there were between-group similarities regarding the number of participants engaged in day, swing, and night shift work, approximately 57% of active duty versus 20% of National Guard/Reserve participants reported operating RPAs on average 51 or more hours a week. This result suggests that active duty operators who participated in the study have a much higher operational tempo.

Combat-related stressors were not rated as within the top sources of stress among participants. Such a finding is helpful for line commanders and medical personnel in understanding occupational stress. However, Chappelle et al. (Ref 8) proposed that such a finding should also be interpreted cautiously when considering individual operators. It is likely that there are Predator/Reaper operators who perceive the deployment of weapons and exposure to live video feed of combat (i.e., destruction/death of enemy combatants and ground forces) as highly stressful even though it is not reported as the main source of occupational stress.

A qualitative analysis also revealed that active duty operators were more likely to report stressors regarding career progression (e.g., undefined promotional path, unclear career incentives, unclear status regarding return to original career field), geographical location (e.g., undesirable environmental location and/or long commute times equal to or longer than 1 hour), and assignment concerns (e.g., the perceived involuntary nature of assignments for many RPA operators, unclear or inconsistent reports regarding assignment opportunities in the future). The stressors of career progression, geographical location, and the perceived involuntary nature of assignments are organizational leadership decisions. Consequently, most of the stressors were operational in nature and/or based upon leadership decisions and policies rather than combat related. The findings of this research suggest active duty operators who participated in this study were experiencing a greater breadth and depth of occupational stressors than National Guard/Reserve operators.

5.2. Facets of Occupational Burnout (Active Duty vs. National Guard/Reserve Units)

The second objective of this study was to assess for differences between active duty and National Guard/Reserve units regarding the prevalence of high emotional exhaustion and cynicism and low professional sence of efficacy.

As mentioned previously, the subscale of emotional exhaustion is a subjective measure regarding the depletion of emotional energy due to work-related stress. High scores on emotional exhaustion are likely signs of distress in response to emotionally demanding work. According to the results of the study, approximately one out of every five active duty operators reported experiencing high levels of emotional exhaustion. Furthermore, odds ratios revealed that active duty operators were twice as likely to report high levels of high emotional exhaustion when compared with National Guard/Reserve operators. Although a previous study by Chappelle et al. [Ref 8] reported a considerable number of Predator/Reaper operators were at risk for emotional exhaustion, there is a clear difference between active duty and National Guard/Reserve operators. Such prevalence of emotional exhaustion raises aeromedical concerns regarding the impact of such RPA operations on the health and well-being of operators, as well as the elevated risk for a mishap and mission failure [Ref 17,18].

As mentioned previously, the subscale of cynicism is a subjective measure regarding the sense of indifference or a distant attitude towards work (e.g., a declining sense of enthusiasm for work). According to the results of this study, there is a significant difference in the levels of cynicism reported between active duty and National Guard/Reserve operators. Only 7% of National Guard/Reserve operators reported high levels of cynicism as opposed to 17% reported by active duty operators. Note that active duty operators were twice as likely to report high levels of cynicism. There is plausible evidence to suggest that such high levels of cynicism may lead to performance-related difficulties as well as contribute to a high attrition rate. Although the sources of cynicism among active duty operators remain unclear, the higher level of cynicism is, in part, due to reported concern regarding career progression, geographical location, involuntary nature of assignments, and uncertainty regarding future assignments for those who cross-trained with hopes of returning to their original career field.

Despite the higher levels of emotional exhaustion and cynicism, there was no difference in professional efficacy among active duty and National Guard/Reserve operators. Both groups of operators participating in this study are consistent in their sense of accomplishments and effectiveness at work. The higher levels of cynicism and emotional exhaustion are not necessarily associated with a decline in the perception of value on the role of RPA operators and their contribution to critical ISR and precision-strike operations in theater.

6.0. STUDY LIMITATIONS AND RECOMMENDATIONS

The temporal nature and survey methodology of this study raise the concern for sampling error affecting generalizability and external validity of the results. Therefore, generalizability of the results may not be applicable to all USAF Predator/Reaper units, and the causes or influences of occupational burnout may change over time. All Predator/Reaper units will be surveyed again at a later date to confirm study findings and to assess for changes in the prevalence of occupational burnout following implementation of remedial and preventative initiatives.

Another important issue affecting the internal validity is the degree to which the survey methodology allows for definitive judgments about the psychological disposition and service needs of Predator/Reaper operators. As was the case with the study by Chappelle et al. [Ref 8], the survey did not fully address functional impairment of emotional exhaustion and cynicism. Many Predator/Reaper operators who endorse symptoms of emotional exhaustion and cynicism may be functionally resilient and remain aeromedically fit for duty. Nevertheless, the implicit assumption of those endorsing high levels of emotional exhaustion and cynicism is that they need mental health care or medical intervention to mitigate such an unpleasant condition. Further studies to address functional impairment to assess the validity of this implicit assumption are highly recommended.

Regardless of the limitations to external or internal validity of the study due to its operational nature, a significant percentage of Predator/Reaper operators reporting high levels of emotional exhaustion and cynicism within active duty units is likely to benefit from increased access to mental health care. Although the stigma of mental health care is a barrier for many operators, allocating mental health and flight medicine providers within the operational unit of RPA operators may help them overcome such a barrier. Chappelle and McDonald [Ref 16] reported that Predator/Reaper operators experiencing clinical distress were also highly likely to report high levels of emotional exhaustion. Yet, such operators were also highly unlikely to seek mental health care because of concerns that such care would negatively impact their careers.

Assigning a military psychologist with aviation training and a skill set to an RPA unit to interact with operators may help increase access and utilization for mental health care.

Another recommendation is to review active duty units and assess for utilization of appropriate scheduling and fatigue management tools to ensure aircrew are adhering to effective techniques for sustaining "around-the-clock" operations without burning out their most valuable resource (i.e., the human operator). Furthermore, innovations in human-machine technology to reduce cognitive demands and increase efficiency of initiating command and control procedures as well as comfort level will likely help to mitigate risks for occupational burnout.

CONCLUSION

USAF Predator/Reaper operations have emerged as critical assets to ISR and precision-strike operations. These aircraft are relied upon for a wide range of missions throughout the globe. Advances in aviation, computer-based technology, and satellite communication has catapulted USAF remotely piloted aircraft into the center of many operational missions. Although Predator/Reaper aircraft are managed via impressive advances in technology, the most critical component may be the human operator. Safe and effective operations are essential, and line leadership and flight medicine providers should remain vigilant to the impact that technology and operational tempo may have on the psychological health of the human operator.

REFERENCES

[1]   Department of Defense, *Unmanned Aerial Vehicles*, 3 Jun 2003, URL: http://www.defense.gov/specials/uav2002/.

[2]   Drew JG, Shaver R, Lynch KF, Amouzegar MA, Snyder D, Unmanned Aerial Vehicle, End-to-End Support Considerations, Rand Publishing, Santa Monica, CA, Aug 2005.

[3]   Drew C, "Military Is Awash in Data from Drones," *New York Times*, 10 Jan 2010, URL: www.nytimes.com/2010/01/11/business/11drone.html. Accessed 11 Jan 2010.

[4]   Stulberg AN, "Manning the Unmanned Revolution in the U.S. Air Force," *Orbis*, 51(2), Spring 2007, pp. 251-65.

[5]   Deptula D, *Air Force Unmanned Aerial System (UAS) Flight Plan 2009-2047*, Headquarters U.S. Air Force, Washington, DC, 2009, URL: www.af.mil/shared/media/document/AFD090723-034.pdf. Accessed 6 Jan 2010.

[6]   Department of the Air Force, *The U.S. Air Force Remotely Piloted Aircraft and Unmanned Aerial Vehicle Strategic Vision*, Department of the Air Force, Washington, DC, 2005, URL: www.af.mil/shared/media/document/AFD-060322-009.pdf. Accessed 6 Jan 2010.

[7]   Department of Defense, *Office of the Secretary of Defense Unmanned Systems Integrated Roadmap (2009-2034)*, Department of Defense, Washington, DC, 2009, URL: www.jointrobitics.com/documents/library/UMS%20integrated%20Roadmap%202009.pdf. Accessed 6 Jan 2010.

[8]   Chappelle W, Salinas A, McDonald K, "Psychological Health Screening of USAF Remotely Piloted Aircraft (RPA) Operators and Supporting Units," paper presented at the Symposium on Mental Health and Well-Being Across the Military Spectrum, Bergen, Norway, 12 Apr 2011.

[9]   Chappelle W, McDonald K., King RE, Psychological Attributes Critical to the Performance of MQ-1 Predator and MQ-9 Reaper U.S. Air Force Sensor Operators, Technical Report AFRL-SA-BR-TR-2010-0007, USAF School of Aerospace Medicine, Brooks City-Base, TX, Jun 2010.

[10] U.S. Air Force, *Medical Examinations and Standards*, Air Force Instruction 48-123, Department of the Air Force, Washington, DC, 24 Sep 2009, URL: http://www.epublishing.af.mil/shared/media/epubs/AFI48-123.pdf.

[11] Tvaryanas AP, *The Development of Empirically-Based Medical Standards for Large and Weaponized Unmanned Aircraft System Pilots*, Technical Report HSW-PE-BR-TR-2006- 0004, 311th Human Systems Wing, Brooks City-Base, TX, Oct 2006.

[12] Maslach C, Jackson SE, Leiter MP, Maslach Burnout Inventory Manual, 3rd ed., Consulting Psychologists Press, Palo Alto, CA, 1996.

[13] Tvaryanas AP, MacPherson GD, "Fatigue in Pilots of Remotely Piloted Aircraft Before and After Shift Work Adjustment," *Aviation, Space, and Environmental Medicine,* 80(5), May 2009, pp. 454-61.

[14] Thompson WT, Lopez N, Hickey P, DaLuz C, Caldwell JL, Tvaryanas AP, *Effects of Shift Work and Sustained Operations: Operator Performance in Remotely Piloted Aircraft (OP-REPAIR)*, Technical Report HSW-PE-BR-TR-2006-0001, 311th Human Systems Wing, Brooks City-Base, TX, Jan 2006.

[15] Thompson WT, Tvaryanas AP, Constable SH, *U.S. Military Unmanned Aerial Vehicle Mishaps: Assessment of the Role of Human Factors Using Human Factors Analysis and Classification System (HFACS)*, Technical Report HSW-PE-BR-TR-2005-0001, 311th Performance

Enhancement Directorate, Performance Enhancement Research Division, Brooks City-Base, TX, Mar 2005.

[16] Chappelle W, McDonald K, "Occupational Stressors of RPA Operators and Non-Combatant Airmen," unpublished paper presented at the Air Force Research Laboratory Senior Leadership Offsite Conference, Dayton, OH, 3 Mar 2011.

[17] Tvaryanas AP, Thompson WT, Constable SH, "Human Factors in Remotely Piloted Aircraft Operations: HFACS Analysis of 221 Mishaps Over 10 Years," *Aviation, Space, and Environmental Medicine*, 77(7), July 2006, pp. 724-32.

[18] Tvaryanas AP, Thompson WT, "Recurrent Error Pathways in HFACS Data: Analysis of 95 Mishaps with Remotely Piloted Aircraft," *Aviation, Space, and Environmental Medicine*, 79(5), May 2008, pp. 525-32.

INDEX

#

21st century, 103

A

access, 46, 51, 52, 53, 57, 69, 70, 71, 75, 76, 77, 80, 94, 117
accountability, 75
accounting, 57
acquisitions, 103
active- duty pilots, vii, 1
adaptation, 5, 37
advancement(s), 17, 102, 108
aerospace, 22
Afghanistan, 7, 57, 66, 69
age, 109, 110
agencies, 12, 58, 68, 70, 71, 75, 90, 104, 106
anxiety, 106
assessment, 22, 75, 98, 106
assets, viii, 51, 52, 55, 57, 59, 62, 66, 72, 74, 78, 79, 81, 83, 85, 87, 97, 99, 100, 101, 102, 103, 104, 105, 108, 118
ATO, 98, 105
audit, 7, 41, 54, 91
authority, 58
awareness, 104, 105

B

base, 13, 22, 42, 46, 63, 107
benefits, 57
board members, 6, 11, 32, 41
bonuses, 19
burnout, viii, 97, 99, 100, 101, 103, 106, 107, 108, 109, 110, 112, 117, 118

C

CAP, 3, 12, 13, 14, 46
career prospects, 109
category a, 11
category b, 28, 29, 30
certification, 87
challenges, vii, viii, 2, 4, 12, 18, 20, 21, 22, 23, 25, 26, 27, 32, 33, 34, 38, 43, 49, 50, 51, 52, 53, 54, 57, 58, 69, 73, 75, 77, 78, 80, 81, 83, 84, 89, 90, 94
Chief of Staff, 5, 91
children, 110
City, 119, 120
clarity, 24
classes, 61
coding, 44
collaboration, 82, 83
combatants, viii, 25, 97, 99, 100, 102, 103, 105, 106, 108, 115
communication, 22, 79, 86, 89, 108, 118

community(s), 22, 82, 107, 110
competition, 53, 69, 70, 85, 87
compilation, 42
computer, 86, 102, 103, 105, 106, 108, 114, 118
computer systems, 106
conference, 80
conflict, viii, 97, 99, 101
Congress, 3, 6, 31, 32, 36, 41, 47, 52, 71
consensus, 44, 109
construction, 63, 64, 89, 94, 95
content analysis, 41, 43
contingency, 23, 54, 56, 63, 66, 71, 81, 82, 89, 90
conversations, 109
coordination, 57, 78, 82, 84, 85, 87, 88, 90, 105
cost, 19, 45, 54, 57, 59, 64, 67, 89
critical infrastructure, 57
cruise missiles, 101
cycles, 25

D

data collection, 77
decision makers, 51, 57, 59, 64, 68, 83, 86
decision-making process, 50, 84, 85
deficiencies, 59, 68, 73
degradation, 64, 106
demonstrations, 55, 68
denial, 18, 46
Department of Defense, viii, 3, 4, 36, 46, 47, 49, 51, 52, 89, 93, 94, 95, 98, 101, 118, 119
Department of Homeland Security, 70, 93
Department of Transportation, 71
deployments, 14, 51, 69
depression, 106
depth, 102, 105, 106, 115
destruction, viii, 97, 99, 100, 106, 107, 108, 115
disaster, 66
disclosure, 99, 110, 111
discrimination, 21, 104, 106
disposition, 117

distress, 38, 111, 115, 117
draft, 34, 80, 85

E

education, 5, 10, 29, 31, 32, 36, 43, 46
e-mail, 111
emotional exhaustion, viii, 98, 99, 101, 106, 111, 112, 113, 115, 116, 117
employees, 21
employment, 79, 80, 81, 106
endurance, 70, 101, 102
enemy combatants, viii, 98, 99, 102, 103, 105, 108, 115
energy, 101, 106, 111, 115
engineering, 102
environment(s), 4, 9, 17, 18, 19, 51, 71, 73, 85, 87, 100, 106, 107
equipment, 4, 7, 9, 10, 53, 55, 58, 63, 66, 71, 74, 76, 77, 86, 104, 105, 107, 114
ergonomics, 107
evidence, 7, 41, 54, 91, 100, 116
exercise, 73
expertise, 62
exposure, viii, 97, 99, 100, 107, 108, 115
external validity, 117

F

families, 24
federal government, 19
fidelity, 74
fires, 69, 79
fiscal year 2009, 56
flexibility, 9, 102
flight(s), 2, 4, 9, 15, 19, 22, 46, 47, 51, 55, 58, 64, 69, 70, 72, 94, 100, 104, 105, 107, 109, 111, 117, 118
focus groups, viii, 2, 6, 15, 17, 18, 20, 22, 23, 24, 26, 39, 41, 42, 44, 46, 47
force, 4, 46, 50, 60, 66, 68, 70, 82, 86, 108
Fort Hood, 69, 92
freedom, 18, 46, 107

funding, viii, 50, 52, 53, 55, 56, 57, 59, 62, 68, 74, 84, 85, 86, 89
funds, 50, 55, 56, 62, 64, 66, 74, 86, 94

G

GAO, vii, viii, 1, 2, 8, 10, 16, 21, 28, 29, 30, 37, 38, 42, 43, 44, 45, 46, 47, 49, 50, 51, 56, 65, 67, 76, 93, 94, 95
generalizability, 117
Georgia, 92
global communications, 57
growth, 55, 59, 60, 83, 86
guidance, ix, 2, 5, 11, 37, 39, 46, 50, 53, 57, 59, 79, 87, 98, 100, 105

H

harassment, 21
health, 5, 25, 38, 39, 106, 111, 116, 117
health care, 117
health condition, 5, 38
height, 102
history, 22
House, 19, 46, 52
House of Representatives, 52
human, vii, ix, 1, 2, 4, 5, 6, 12, 14, 21, 32, 33, 37, 52, 55, 98, 100, 101, 102, 106, 114, 118
human capital, 2, 5, 37
human-capital, vii, 1, 2, 5, 6, 12, 14, 21, 32, 33, 37
Hunter, 56

I

ideal, 24
identification, 104, 106, 108
illumination, 102, 105
imagery, 102, 103, 104, 105, 107
images, 105, 108
improvements, 111
increased access, 70, 71, 117
individuals, 40, 53

informed consent, 110
infrastructure, vii, viii, 49, 50, 53, 57, 59, 67, 68, 76, 77, 83, 84, 86, 89
integration, 4, 52, 53, 62, 70, 73, 74, 76, 77, 79, 82, 104, 105
intelligence, viii, 4, 7, 9, 55, 57, 58, 97, 98, 99, 100, 104
interface, 114
internal validity, 117
interoperability, 74, 78, 88
intervention, 117
investment(s), 19, 32, 52, 54, 55, 83, 87, 89
Iowa, 8
Iraq, viii, 7, 50, 54, 57, 61, 66, 69, 89, 90, 93
issues, 21, 22, 36, 38, 43, 53, 57, 77, 107

J

justification, 17, 89, 95

K

kill, 26

L

lack of control, 109
laws, 39
lead, 64, 106, 107, 108, 111, 116
leadership, viii, 13, 14, 22, 32, 39, 43, 82, 97, 99, 100, 103, 111, 115, 118
life cycle, 57, 59, 68, 89
light, viii, 50, 54, 89, 90, 105
logging, 46
Louisiana, 71

M

magnitude, 112, 113
majority, viii, 98, 99
man, 50, 66

management, 5, 32, 37, 38, 45, 52, 57, 68, 75, 82, 90, 94, 117
manpower, 46, 59, 62, 107
Marine Corps, 7, 9, 55, 56, 65, 77, 82, 92, 94
marital status, 110
materials, 80
matter, 58, 81
MBI, 98, 110, 111
measurement, 110
media, 118, 119
medical, 22, 46, 111, 115, 117
medical care, 46
medicine, 100, 109, 111, 117, 118
mental health, 26, 111, 117
mental image, 106
mental imagery, 106
mental representation, 104
mentor, 12
methodology, 6, 54, 110, 117
Mexico, 9
military, 5, 7, 10, 19, 29, 30, 31, 32, 37, 43, 46, 47, 51, 52, 53, 55, 56, 57, 58, 61, 65, 66, 69, 70, 71, 73, 77, 78, 79, 80, 81, 82, 83, 84, 85, 87, 88, 89, 90, 94, 100, 104, 106, 114, 117
mission(s), viii, 2, 4, 7, 8, 9, 10, 12, 13, 15, 17, 18, 19, 20, 23, 26, 32, 33, 34, 35, 46, 50, 52, 54, 55, 61, 65, 66, 69, 71, 73, 76, 79, 82, 84, 85, 86, 87, 90, 97, 99, 100, 101, 102, 103, 104, 105, 108, 116, 118
morale, 3, 5, 21, 22, 23, 38, 43, 111
motivation, 21
MQ-1 Predator, vii, viii, 1, 4, 13, 15, 48, 97, 99, 100, 101, 102, 103, 104, 119
MQ-9 Reaper, v, viii, 13, 48, 97, 99, 100, 101, 102, 103, 104, 119
multiple factors, 29

N

national airspace, 53, 57, 69, 70, 71, 72, 75, 76, 77
national borders, 108

National Defense Authorization Act, 4, 45, 71
national security, 17, 106
negative effects, 26, 33, 34, 35, 107
Norway, 119

O

obstacles, 52
occupational burnout, viii, 97, 99, 100, 101, 103, 106, 107, 108, 109, 110, 112, 117, 118
Office of Management and Budget, 54, 59, 89, 93, 94, 95
officials, vii, 1, 2, 5, 6, 9, 13, 14, 15, 17, 18, 19, 20, 21, 22, 24, 26, 30, 31, 37, 38, 39, 40, 41, 45, 54, 60, 61, 63, 64, 66, 69, 70, 71, 73, 74, 77, 79, 80, 81, 82, 89, 90, 91, 94
OH, 120
opportunities, ix, 10, 17, 18, 32, 33, 46, 51, 53, 73, 74, 77, 82, 85, 87, 88, 98, 100, 107, 115
optimism, 15

P

Pacific, 92
participants, 41, 42, 43, 47, 87, 99, 109, 110, 111, 114, 115
percentile, 40, 47
personal efficacy, 107
personal relations, 111
personal relationship, 111
personality, 105
personality traits, 105
physical health, 47
physicians, 100, 109, 111
pipeline, 60, 61
platform, 58, 88
policy, viii, 6, 33, 46, 50, 57, 63, 76, 106
pools, 63
positive relationship, 29
post-traumatic stress disorder, 38

precision-strike operations, viii, 97, 99, 101, 116, 118
preparedness, 66
President, 56, 89
principles, 3, 54, 75, 90
private sector, 20
probability, 60
procurement, 89
professional development, 38, 46
professionals, 6, 39
programming, 4, 55
project, 46, 76
promotion rates, vii, 1, 3, 5, 6, 27, 28, 30, 31, 32, 36, 39, 40, 43, 45, 47
protection, 66, 108
psychiatric diagnosis, 106
psychological distress, 107
psychological health, ix, 98, 100, 107, 109, 118
psychological well-being, 101
psychologist, 22, 25, 117

Q

qualifications, 52
quality of life, vii, 1, 5, 25, 26, 33, 34, 35, 38, 39, 43
questionnaire, 110, 111

R

race, 11
radar, 98, 102
RE, 119
recommendations, ix, 2, 6, 11, 25, 34, 38, 39, 50, 71, 85, 98, 100
recovery, 10, 104
recruiting, 2, 12, 18, 19, 20, 21, 22, 33, 34, 37
Reform, 93
regression, 29, 41
regulations, 87
reliability, 57

remotely piloted aircraft, vii, viii, 2, 3, 37, 42, 97, 98, 99, 100, 118
requirements, viii, 12, 13, 14, 15, 18, 19, 20, 32, 35, 46, 50, 52, 53, 56, 57, 58, 59, 61, 62, 63, 64, 67, 68, 69, 70, 73, 74, 75, 76, 77, 83, 85, 87, 89, 93, 94
researchers, 3, 6, 22, 25, 38, 39
reserves, 101, 106, 111
resource allocation, 60
resources, 51, 57, 60, 61, 68, 75, 77, 83, 85, 86, 87, 107
response, 3, 4, 6, 22, 25, 33, 34, 35, 38, 39, 46, 111, 115
restrictions, 53, 70, 85, 87
retention rate, 20
rhythm, 26
risk(s), viii, 15, 17, 19, 25, 32, 33, 34, 50, 57, 59, 65, 66, 84, 86, 97, 99, 100, 106, 107, 108, 109, 116, 118
routines, 107
RPA pilots, vii, viii, 1, 2, 3, 5, 6, 8, 9, 10, 12, 13, 14, 15, 17, 18, 19, 20, 21, 22, 23, 24, 25, 26, 27, 28, 29, 30, 31, 32, 33, 34, 35, 36, 37, 38, 39, 40, 41, 42, 43, 44, 45, 46, 47, 105
rules, 98, 104

S

safety, 2, 15, 17, 25, 32, 33, 34, 47, 70, 100, 103
sampling error, 117
school, 14, 29, 32
scope, 6, 47, 54
Secretary of Defense, 12, 13, 17, 19, 20, 33, 37, 38, 46, 47, 76, 77, 84, 85, 87, 89, 91, 119
security, 57, 74
Senate, 4
sensors, 7, 55, 102, 105
services, viii, 7, 10, 17, 19, 50, 51, 52, 53, 55, 56, 57, 58, 60, 64, 65, 68, 70, 71, 73, 76, 78, 80, 81, 82, 83, 84, 85, 87, 88, 89, 91, 95
sex, 11

shape, 12
signals, 53, 66
signs, 111, 115
simulation, 73, 75, 76, 85, 87
software, 74
solution, 70
Spring, 118
staffing, 14, 25, 27, 33, 35
stakeholders, 54, 57, 78, 79, 80, 83, 85
standard deviation, 98, 113
state(s), 2, 8, 11, 15, 17, 24, 31, 66, 71, 86, 87, 93
stigma, 18, 19, 110, 117
storage, 63
strategic position, 104
stress, viii, 5, 22, 23, 24, 25, 26, 35, 38, 43, 98, 99, 101, 107, 109, 110, 111, 113, 114, 115
stressors, viii, 24, 26, 35, 98, 99, 100, 101, 107, 108, 109, 114, 115
structure, 68
substitutes, 80
supervisors, 11
support staff, 15
surveillance, viii, 4, 7, 9, 55, 65, 69, 97, 98, 99, 100, 102, 104, 105
suspense, 107
symptoms, 117
synchronize, 51, 62, 68, 73, 75, 77, 83, 84, 85

T

tactics, viii, 49, 51, 53, 54, 58, 73, 78, 79, 80, 81, 82, 83, 87, 90, 98, 104, 105, 106
talent, 37
target, 2, 25, 46, 65, 74, 102, 104, 105
target identification, 105
Task Force, 70, 76, 77
team members, 42
teams, 22
technical comments, 34, 85
techniques, viii, 49, 51, 53, 54, 58, 78, 79, 80, 81, 82, 87, 90, 98, 104, 106, 118

technology, 55, 58, 68, 70, 76, 77, 93, 102, 108, 118
temperature, 107
tempo, viii, 43, 97, 99, 100, 115, 118
term plans, 63
territory, 71
testing, 71
threats, 100, 103
time frame, 15
total costs, 64
training programs, 51, 53, 78, 83, 84, 88
transport, 64

U

UAS, vii, viii, 49, 50, 51, 52, 53, 55, 56, 57, 58, 59, 60, 61, 62, 63, 64, 65, 66, 67, 68, 69, 70, 71, 72, 73, 74, 75, 76, 77, 78, 79, 80, 81, 82, 83, 84, 85, 86, 87, 88, 89, 90, 92, 93, 94, 95, 118
UAS operations, vii, viii, 49, 50, 51, 53, 54, 57, 60, 61, 62, 63, 64, 65, 66, 67, 69, 78, 79, 80, 83, 84, 86, 90
United, v, viii, 1, 3, 4, 8, 9, 25, 49, 50, 51, 54, 57, 61, 66, 70, 71, 90, 93, 94
United States, v, viii, 1, 3, 4, 8, 9, 25, 49, 50, 51, 54, 57, 61, 66, 70, 71, 90, 93, 94
unmanned aerial systems, vii, 1, 37
Unmanned Aerial Vehicles, 118
unmanned aircraft systems, viii, 4, 37, 49, 51, 52, 89
updating, 15, 32, 87

V

variables, 31
vehicles, 101
versatility, 102
vision, 60, 62, 82, 103
vulnerability, 50

W

waiver, 64

Washington, 45, 47, 92, 93, 94, 118, 119
weapons, 9, 14, 74, 102, 103, 104, 105, 106, 115
wear, 64
well-being, 116
wellness, 5, 38
White Paper, 47, 48
workers, 47

workforce, 5, 12, 13, 15, 17, 18, 32, 37
working conditions, vii, 1, 3, 5, 20, 23, 25, 33, 38, 39, 47
working hours, 20
workload, vii, 1, 15, 107
work-related stress, 106, 111, 115
worldwide, 100